Co-ordinated
SCIENCE
Biology

Brian Beckett
RoseMarie Gallagher

Oxford University Press

Contents

INTRODUCTION

Everything in this book has been organized to help you find things quickly and easily. It is written in two-page units. Each unit is about a topic that you are likely to study.

● The full colour 'core' pages provide a straightforward presentation of important facts and concepts. The extension material is presented in an interactive form. Text set in italics invites you to recall knowledge and relate it to what you are reading, identify problems, formulate hypotheses, make predictions, interpret data and draw conclusions.

● Use the contents page
If you are looking for information on a large topic, look it up in the contents list. But if you cannot see the topic you want then:

● Use the index
If there is something small you want to check on, look up the most likely word in the index. The index gives the page number where you'll find more information about that word.

● Test yourself
There are questions at the end of each topic. They are classified under headings such as factual recall, understanding, data interpretation, hypothesis formulation and making predictions.

We hope that when you complete this book you will have a greater understanding of what biology is about, and will have enjoyed studying it.

Brian Beckett
Rose Marie Gallagher

1·1 Living things

You are a **living thing**. Grass, whales, and bats are living things too. But stones and rain are non-living things. Living things are different from non-living things in the ways shown below.

Living things move and have senses

Plants move by growing, like these beans growing up bean poles. They don't have sense organs but they can still respond to things. Roots grow down in response to gravity, and to find water. Shoots grow up towards light.

Animals walk, or run, or hop, or crawl, or swim, or fly. They find their way using **sense organs**. These are eyes, ears, noses, taste buds, skin, and insect feelers called **antennae**.

Living things feed

They need food for energy, growth, and repair.

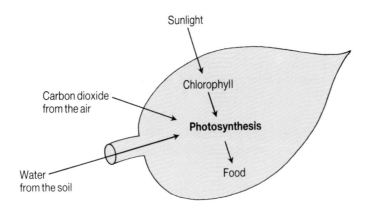

Sunlight

Chlorophyll

Carbon dioxide from the air

Photosynthesis

Water from the soil

Food

Plants make their own food in their leaves. This is called **photosynthesis**. It needs light, water, carbon dioxide, and a green chemical called **chlorophyll** which is found in leaves.

Animals can't make their own food so they eat plants and other animals. Which animal is this? What is it eating?

Living things respire

They get energy from food by a process called **respiration**. This usually needs oxygen.

Food + Oxygen ⟹ ENERGY + Waste: water and carbon dioxide

Living things excrete

All living things produce waste. The removal of waste from their bodies is called **excretion**.

Plants store waste in old leaves, which fall in the autumn.

Animals excrete through their lungs and kidneys, and through their skin when they sweat.

Living things reproduce and grow

Animals lay eggs, or have babies. Seeds from plants grow into new plants.

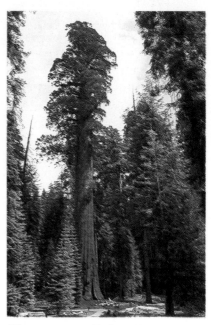

Plants grow all their lives. This giant redwood tree has been growing for over 2000 years!

Animals stop growing when they reach their adult size.

Questions

1. Name seven ways in which living things are different from non-living things.
2. Name the green stuff, and three other things plants need to make food.
3. Name all your sense organs.
4. What is:
   a) respiration?
   b) excretion?

1·2 Living things and their needs

Our planet is a huge ball of rock spinning in circles around the sun. Below is a photograph of it taken from outer space.

This huge ball of rock is home for countless billions of living creatures. They can live on it because it has the six things which living creatures need.

Sun

Light and heat

Light and carbon dioxide

The sun's light provides energy for all living things. Plants need light, and carbon dioxide from the air, to make food by photosynthesis. Animals get their energy by eating plants, or by eating animals which eat plants.

Warmth

If it gets too hot or too cold the chemical changes which are necessary for life will stop. In many parts of the Earth temperatures lie between 25°C and 30°C. Most living things are adapted to live at these temperatures.

Water

Our world has plenty of water. All living things need water because the chemical changes necessary for life take place in it. Our bodies are three quarters water.

Oxygen

Air is about one fifth oxygen. Most living things need oxygen to get energy from their food by respiration.

Minerals

The Earth's soils contain minerals. These are essential for health and growth. Plants take in minerals through their roots. Animals get minerals by eating plants or other animals.

The biosphere

The **biosphere** is all those parts of the Earth's surface where living things are found. In fact they are found almost everywhere from about 9000 metres up mountains to at least 5000 metres under the sea.

This diagram shows a slice through the biosphere, from the highest to the lowest places where creatures can live.

Life on land

Springtails and mites can live up to 9000 metres feeding on pollen and seeds carried up by the wind.

Most flowering plants stop at about 6000 metres. Mosses and lichens can live much higher up.

Humans keep animals and grow crops up to 4500 metres.

Conifer forests stop at about 1500 metres. Deciduous forests stop at about 1000 metres.

Life in water

Deep water has an upper sunlit zone where photosynthesis is possible, and a dark lower zone.

In clear water the sunlit zone can be up to 100 metres deep. Millions of tiny plant-like creatures called **phytoplankton** live here. They are eaten by tiny animals called **zooplankton**.

Both types of plankton are eaten by larger creatures such as fish.

The pitch dark lower zone is home to creatures which live on dead and living things which fall from the sunlit zone above, as well as cast off skins, droppings etc.

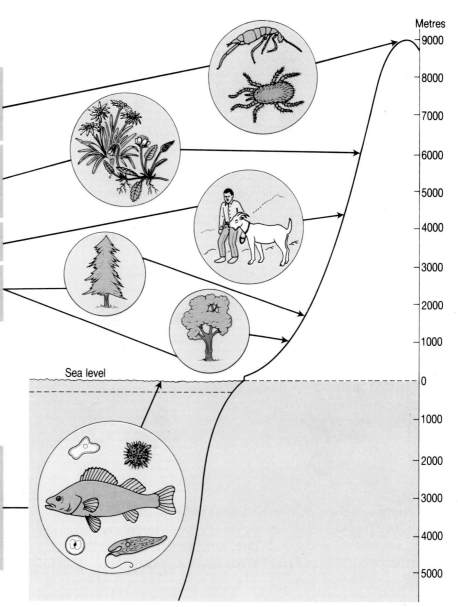

Question

The Earth is home to billions of creatures but there are no living things on the moon. Write down the six things needed for life. Which of them do you think are found on the moon and which are not?

1·3 Sorting and naming

Spiny anteater.

Jumping spider.

These are just two of the things that live on Earth. Altogether there are over one-and-a-half million different kinds of living thing!

To make it easier to study them biologists sort living things into groups which are alike in some way. Try sorting the six creatures below into groups. Do this now.

You could sort them into those found on land, in the air, and in water. But this would group together very different creatures like crabs, sea weeds, and fish. Would it make sense to sort them according to colour and size? What other ways are there of sorting them?

Biologists first sort living things into three large groups. The three large groups are:

1 Simple organisms	2 Plants	3 Animals

These huge groups are then split into smaller groups. You can see how this is done in the rest of this chapter.

Naming living things

If you want to find the name of a plant or animal you could look through books until you see a picture of it. Or you could use a **key**.

Keys

The simplest keys are made up of short, numbered sentences arranged in pairs. Look at the example below. Read the instructions, then use this key to name the insects drawn on this page.

How to use the key

Read the first pair of descriptions and decide which fit the insect you are trying to name. Opposite the description you choose there is a number. This number tells you which pair of descriptions to read next. Read them, and again decide which describes the insect. Opposite, you will find either the insect's name, or the number of the next pair of descriptions to read. Carry on until you find the insect's name.

An example of a key

1	Wings visible	3
	Wings not visible	2
2	Three-pronged tail	Bristle tail
	Pincers at end of tail	Earwig
3	Two pairs of wings	4
	One pair of wings	5
4	Wings fringed with hairs	Thrip
	Wings not fringed with hairs	6
5	Legs longer than body	Cranefly
	Legs not longer than body	Housefly
6	Wings larger than body	Butterfly
	Wings not larger than body	Wasp

1·4 Groups of living things

In this unit you can see how living things are first sorted into huge groups, which are then split into smaller and smaller groups.

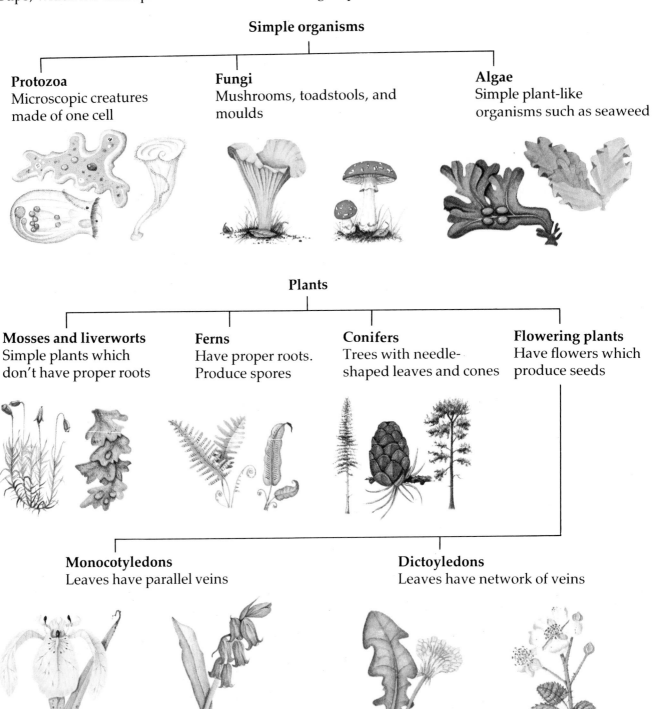

Simple organisms

Protozoa
Microscopic creatures made of one cell

Fungi
Mushrooms, toadstools, and moulds

Algae
Simple plant-like organisms such as seaweed

Plants

Mosses and liverworts
Simple plants which don't have proper roots

Ferns
Have proper roots. Produce spores

Conifers
Trees with needle-shaped leaves and cones

Flowering plants
Have flowers which produce seeds

Monocotyledons
Leaves have parallel veins

Dictoyledons
Leaves have network of veins

Animals without backbones (Invertebrates)

Coelenterates
Sack-like body
with tentacles

Flatworms
Flat body covered
with cilia

Annelid worms
Body encircled with
many rings

Molluscs
One coiled shell or
two uncoiled shells

Arthropods

Crustaceans
Hard outer
skeleton

Insects
Six legs and usually
two pairs of wings

Arachnids
Eight legs.
No wings

Myriapods
Many pairs of
legs

Animals with backbones (Vertebrates)

Fish
Scales, fins, and gills

Amphibia
live in water and
on land

Reptiles
Covered with
hard, dry scales

Birds
Covered with
feathers. Wings

Mammals
Hairy skin.
Young feed on
mother's milk

Questions

1   What is the word for:
    a) animals with backbones?
    b) animals without backbones?

2   Do fungi belong to the plant group?

3   Which group do you belong to?
4   Which animals have four pairs of legs?
5   Which plants don't have flowers?
6   What is a dicotyledon?

1·5 Simple organisms

Protozoa

Protozoa are tiny creatures. Some are so small you could get thousands of them on the head of a pin. You need a microscope to see them properly. Some protozoa feed on other tiny creatures. Others contain chlorophyll, and can make their own food, like plants do. *Amoeba*, *Paramecium*, and *Euglena* are protozoa.

This is an *Amoeba*. It moves by changing its shape. It feeds on bacteria and other tiny creatures.

Paramecium has tiny hairs called cilia all over it. These trap its food and help it move.

Euglena can make its own food, like plants do, because it contains chlorophyll. That's what makes it green.

Fungi

Mushrooms, toadstools, mildews, and moulds are all **fungi**. Some fungi look a bit like plants, but they cannot make their own food. Some fungi feed on dead things, like the remains of plants and animals. They are called **saprophytes**. Others feed on living things, and cause disease. They are called **parasites**. Ringworm in humans and mildew in plants are caused by parasitic fungi.

These mushrooms are fungi you can eat. Mushrooms do not need light, so some people grow them in cellars for sale to shops.

This is a poisonous fungus called a Fly Agaric. It is common in pine and birch woods. If eaten in large amounts it can kill you.

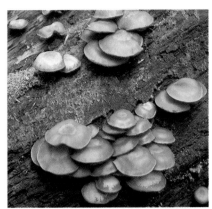

Bracket fungi kill trees, then digest the dead wood. You usually see them on dead trees.

All fungi are made up of fine threads called **hyphae** (pronounced hi-fee). It is easy to see the hyphae in moulds, but in mushrooms and toadstools hyphae are packed tightly together.

Fungi reproduce by forming **spores.** These are tiny cells that get scattered by the wind. When they land in the right place they grow into more fungi.

Bread mould growing on a piece of bread. The white threads are the hyphae. Each black dot contains thousands of spores.

These are puff-ball fungi. When a drop of rain hits the puff-ball, a cloud of spores shoots out.

Algae

Algae are like plants because they make their own food by photosynthesis. But they are not really plants because they do not have proper roots, stems, or leaves.

Seaweeds are large algae that grow in the sea. They can be brown, green, or red. This type is called bladderwrack.

The green scum you sometimes see floating on ponds is made of tiny algae called Spirogyra. If you look at Spirogyra under a microscope you will see lots of tiny green threads. They are covered with slime which stops them getting tangled.

Questions

1 What are protozoa?
2 Name a protozoan that can make its own food.
3 Some fungi are saprophytes. What does this mean?
4 Are mushrooms saprophytes or parasites?

5 How do fungi reproduce?
6 In what way are algae like plants?
7 In what way are algae different from plants?
8 Name two kinds of algae. Where are these algae found?

In this unit and the next, we look at groups of animals without backbones that you met on page 7. Animals without backbones are called **invertebrates**.

Coelenterates

Hydra, jellyfish, and sea anemones are all **coelenterates**. A coelenterate has a body like a bag. The open end is the mouth. It has tentacles round it to catch small animals for food. The tentacles have sting cells to sting the animals and paralyse them.

Hydra lives in ponds. It moves by turning cartwheels. It grows buds which break off to form new hydra.

This is a sea anemone. It uses sting cells on its tentacles to paralyse small creatures which are then pushed into its mouth.

Jellyfish live in the sea. They move by opening and closing like an umbrella. Some have sting cells which can hurt swimmers.

Flatworms

Flatworms have flat bodies with a mouth at one end. Freshwater flatworms, tapeworms, and flukes all belong to this group.

Fresh water flatworms live in ponds and streams. They move by waving tiny hairs called cilia.

Flukes live inside other animals, and can cause disease. This shows a liver fluke on a sheep's liver. It hangs on by suckers. It can kill the sheep.

Tapeworms live in the guts of other animals, and eat their digested food. This one lives in humans. It can grow up to eight metres long.

Annelid worms

These have bodies made of rings, or **segments**. They are sometimes called true worms. Examples are earthworms, lugworms, and leeches.

Earthworms 'eat' soil and digest tiny creatures and dead leaves in it. The rest passes through their bodies.

Leeches live on other animals and suck their blood. One type is used by surgeons to clean up infected flesh round wounds.

Lugworms live under sand on the seashore. They suck in sea water and eat any tiny creatures in it.

Molluscs

Snails, mussels, and octopuses are all molluscs. Molluscs have soft bodies. Most have one or two shells.

Snails have coiled shells. They move about on a slimy flat foot. They have long rough tongues for scraping up food.

A mussel has two shells hinged together. It anchors itself to rock by tough threads. It feeds on tiny creatures in sea water.

An octopus has a shell inside its body. It uses tentacles with suckers to move and to catch food.

Questions

1 Which group of animals has a body like a bag?
2 How do coelenterates feed themselves?
3 What do tapeworms eat?
4 What is the difference between flatworms and annelid worms?
5 Give another name for annelid worms.
6 Name three kinds of annelid worm.
7 Write down two features of mollucsc. Name two molluscs.
8 How do snails eat?

1·7 Look no backbones! II

Let's look now at the largest group of animals without backbones – the **arthropods**. Spiders, flies, and shrimps are all arthropods. Arthropods have a tough skin called a **cuticle**. They have jointed legs, and most have feelers or **antennae**. They can have simple eyes with only one lens, or **compound eyes** with thousands of lenses. They are divided into four smaller groups.

Crustaceans

Crabs, lobsters, shrimps, woodlice, and waterfleas are **crustaceans**. Crustaceans have two pairs of antennae.

Crabs have a thick, hard cuticle and five pairs of legs.

Woodlice have a thin cuticle and live in damp places.

Like all flies, the horsefly is an arthropod. Look at its eyes. They are compound eyes, made up of thousands of tiny lenses.

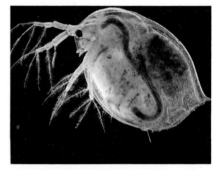

In waterfleas the cuticle is quite thin and soft.

Insects

For every person alive there are about a million insects! About 700 000 different kinds are known. Insects' bodies have three parts: a **head**, a **thorax**, and an **abdomen**.

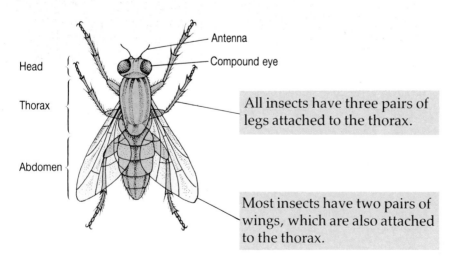

Head

Thorax

Abdomen

Antenna

Compound eye

All insects have three pairs of legs attached to the thorax.

Most insects have two pairs of wings, which are also attached to the thorax.

Name as many parts of this horsefly as you can, by comparing it with the diagram opposite.

Many insects cause harm. Some destroy crops. Some spread disease. For example mosquitos spread malaria among humans. Some are a nuisance, like the midges that bite you in summer, and moths that damage clothes.

Many insects undergo big changes during their lives. Every butterfly was once a caterpillar. Every housefly was a maggot!

Colorado beetles are feared by potato growers because they destroy potato crops.

Many butterflies are brightly coloured. Scientists think they might use their colours to signal to each other.

Arachnids

Arachnids are arthropods with four pairs of legs, and no antennae. They use poison fangs to paralyse their prey. Spiders, harvestmen, mites, ticks, and scorpions are all arachnids.

Spiders are the most common arachnids. Many of them spin webs or tripwires of silk, to catch their prey.

A scorpion ready to strike. Its sting is in its tail. The sting from some scorpions can kill humans.

Myriapods

The word 'myriapod' means 'many pairs of feet'. Myriapods have long bodies made up of many segments. Each segment has at least one pair of legs. Centipedes and millipedes are myriapods.

Centipedes have one pair of legs to each segment. They paralyse their prey with poison fangs.

Millipedes have two pairs of legs to each segment. They eat plants.

Questions

1 Which group of arthropods has:
   a) three pairs of legs?
   b) four pairs of legs?
   c) two pairs of antennae?

2 Give two reasons why spiders are not insects.
3 Name two kinds of myriapod.
4 Name the three parts of an insect's body.

In this unit and the next, we look at the groups of animals with backbones. These are called **vertebrates**. There are five groups of vertebrates:

| fish | amphibians | reptiles | birds | mammals |

You belong to the last group!

Fish

The body of a fish is smooth and streamlined for easy movement through water. Fish are covered with scales, like the tiles on a roof.

Most fish are weightless in water, because their bodies contain a bladder like a balloon which buoys them up.

A fish swims by moving its tail from side to side.

The scales on a trout's body.

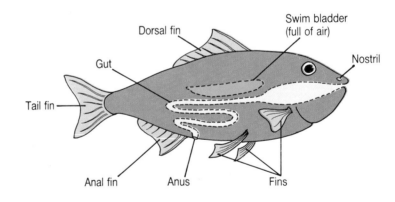

The parts of a fish.

Most female fish, like this trout, reproduce by laying eggs.

But these pregnant guppies will give birth to live baby fish.

A baby dogfish is born in a capsule with a sac of food.

Amphibians

Frogs, toads, salamanders, and newts are all **amphibians**.

Amphibians have four limbs and moist skin. They can live both on land and in water. On land they breathe using lungs. In water they breathe through their skin.

Amphibians lay their eggs in water. These hatch into tadpoles, which swim using tails, and breathe through gills.

This frog has just laid her eggs as frog spawn. In about a week they'll become tadpoles.

Newts live on land for part of the year. But in spring they move into the water to breed.

Reptiles

Lizards, crocodiles, snakes, and tortoises are reptiles. Reptiles have tough, dry, scaly skin. They breathe with lungs. They lay eggs with tough shells like leather.

A snake egg hatches... and out comes the snake's head.

Crocodiles look peaceful and lazy. But don't be fooled...

Some snakes won't harm you. But a viper like this one can kill.

Questions

1 Fish are streamlined. How does this help them?

2 How do fish breathe?

3 How do fish swim?

4 How is a tadpole different from a frog?

5 Explain how frogs can live on land and in water.

6 Do all reptiles have legs?

7 How are reptile eggs different from bird eggs?

8 Name two amphibians and two reptiles.

1·9 Animals with backbones II

Let's now look at the last two groups of animals with backbones – birds and mammals. Birds and mammals are **warm blooded**. This means their bodies always stay around the same temperature, no matter what the weather is like. All other animals are **cold blooded**. Their bodies get hot and cold with the weather.

Birds

All birds have feathers on their bodies. They also have wings, but not all birds can fly. They have beaks for pecking and tearing food. They lay eggs covered with a hard shell.

Like all birds, penguins have wings – but they cannot fly.

Birds have light hollow bones, to help them fly.

Water birds live on fish and other water creatures...

...but this tawny owl is about to dine on a mouse.

Mammals

Mammals have hair on their bodies. Female mammals have breasts, or **mammary glands**, from which their young ones suck milk. There are three kinds of mammals.

Mammals that lay eggs

Mammals that lay eggs are called **monotremes**. The spiny ant-eater, duck-billed platypus, and opossum are monotremes.

When monotreme eggs hatch the babies are not fully formed. They are fed on milk for several weeks while their missing parts grow.

The duck-billed platypus lays its eggs in an underground nest.

Mammals with pouches

Some mammals carry their young in a pouch. They are called **marsupials**. Kangaroos, wallabies, and koalas are marsupials.

Baby marsupials start growing in their mother's womb. Before they are fully formed they crawl out of the womb and into her pouch. The pouch has a teat in it from which the young suck milk.

A kangaroo carrying her baby in her pouch.

Placental mammals

Humans, bats, whales, horses, and sheep are all placental mammals. That means their young develop inside the mother's womb until they are fully formed.

Young are attached to the wall of the womb by a **placenta**. Food and oxygen pass through the placenta from the mother's blood.

Baby rabbits are born below ground, in fur-lined nests.

Bats are the only mammals that can fly. A baby bat clings to its mother until it is about two weeks old. Then she hangs it upside down in a safe place while she flies off to find food.

Sea lions are placental mammals too. The pups are suckled until they are about three months old.

Questions

1 Name two things that help birds fly.
2 Name a bird that can't fly.
3 What do human mothers and kangaroo mothers have in common?
4 What are monotremes? Give two examples.
5 Think of two reasons why pouches might be better than eggs, for developing babies.
6 Write down ten examples of placental mammals.
7 Think of three advantages of a mother carrying babies inside her rather than laying eggs.

1·10 Plants

There are two kinds of plants:

1 Plants without seeds. These are mosses, liverworts, and ferns. They produce **spores** which grow into new plants.

2 Seed plants. These are conifers and flowering plants. They produce **seeds** which grow into new plants.

Plants without seeds (non-flowering plants)

Mosses and liverworts. These usually grow in damp places. Their spores grow in **capsules** on the end of stalks.

Moss plants have stems and tiny leaves. Over 600 different kinds grow in Britain. This one is called bank hair moss.

Moss capsules. When they are ripe their lids drop off, releasing spores which are scattered by the wind.

Unlike mosses, many liverworts have no distinct stems. They look like leaves growing flat on the ground.

Ferns. These usually grow in woods and other damp shady places. Their spores grow in capsules attached to the back of the leaves.

Britain has over 50 different kinds of fern. This one is called hard fern. It is common on moorland and heath.

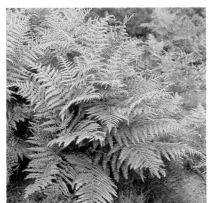

This kind of fern is called bracken. It can grow nearly two metres tall. It is very common on moorland.

Groups of spore capsules on the back of a fern leaf. Each group is protected by a tiny orange-brown scale leaf.

Seed plants

Conifers. Pines, spruces, larches, cedars, and firs are conifers. They produce male and female cones.

The male pine cone produces pollen, which is carried by the wind to a female cone.

The fertilized female cone grows seeds under its flaps, which open when they are ripe.

Flowering plants. Cabbages, horsechestnut trees, and grasses are all flowering plants. They have flowers with reproductive organs which produce seeds. There are two kinds of flowering plants, **monocotyledons** and **dicotyledons**.

Monocotyledons, like these daffodils, have long thin leaves with parallel veins.

Dicotyledons, like this water lily, have broad leaves with a network of veins.

A horsechestnut tree in flower. Its hard brown seeds are used in the game of 'conkers'.

Questions

1   What are capsules, cones, and flowers for?
2   Which of these plants have capsules? Which have cones? Which have flowers?
    roses, bog moss, Christmas trees, bracken ferns.

3   Which of these are monocotyledons, and which are dicotyledons?
    buttercups, tulips, grasses, apple trees.
    Explain your answer.
4   Name the two main groups of plant.

1·A Metabolism and enzymes

Metabolism

Your body is a chemical factory. At any moment up to 1000 different chemical reactions are taking place inside it. Together, these reactions are called **metabolism**. They each play some part in keeping you alive and well. So, metabolism is **all the chemical reactions necessary for life**.

What do you think happens to your metabolism when you run, and when you sleep?

Metabolism speeds up when you are active, and slows down when you sleep. **Basal metabolism** is the slowest metabolism needed to keep you alive. This is just enough to maintain breathing, heart beat and other vital processes. There are two types of metabolism.

Catabolism. This is a type of metabolism in which substances with complex molecules are broken down into simpler molecules to **release energy** for life. All living things obtain energy by a type of catabolism called **respiration**. This uses oxygen to break down food such as glucose sugar into carbon dioxide and water and **releases energy**.

What does your body do with the energy released by respiration? Think of a way some of this energy is lost before it can be used. Study the diagram below after you have some answers.

Anabolism. This is the opposite of catabolism. Anabolism *uses* energy from catabolism to build up complex molecules from simpler ones. For example energy is used to make starch molecules out of glucose, and proteins from amino acids. Now study the photographs on the right.

Anabolism is driven by energy from catabolism, and uses materials from food to make all the substances the body needs.

In the picture above which person do you think has the lowest basal metabolism, and the highest rate of anabolism? Give reasons for your answers.

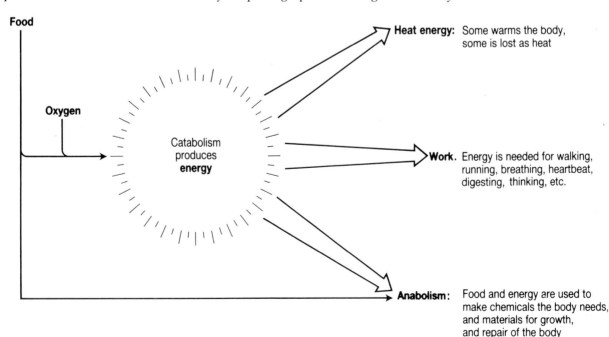

Food

Oxygen

Catabolism produces **energy**

Heat energy: Some warms the body, some is lost as heat

Work. Energy is needed for walking, running, breathing, heartbeat, digesting, thinking, etc.

Anabolism: Food and energy are used to make chemicals the body needs, and materials for growth, and repair of the body

Enzymes

The chemical reactions of metabolism would go very slowly or not at all if it were not for **enzymes**. An enzyme speeds up chemical reactions inside living things, but the enzyme itself is not used up in the reaction so it can do the same thing over and over again.

Enzymes:

1 are needed in catabolism to break down molecules to release energy;

2 are needed in digestion to break down the food we eat into liquid which can be absorbed into the body;

3 are needed in anabolism to put simple molecules together and make complex ones.

Pepsin is an enzyme which digests proteins. It can change solid egg white into a liquid. Test tubes were prepared to study pepsin.

TUBE 1 37°C	TUBE 2 20°C	TUBE 3 0°C	TUBE 4 37°C	TUBE 5 37°C
Egg white	Egg white	Egg white	Egg white	Egg white
Pepsin	Pepsin	Pepsin	Pepsin	Boiled pepsin
Weak acid	Weak acid	Weak acid	Weak alkali	Weak acid

(What control test tubes would have been prepared as well?)

Results:

1 Egg white disappeared from tube 1 in 25 minutes and from tube 2 in 50 minutes.

2 After two hours the egg white remained solid and unchanged in all the other tubes.

From these results you can work out some of the features of pepsin for yourself. These features are shared by other enzymes. How, for example, is pepsin affected by temperature, acid and alkali? Try to do this before reading the summary of enzyme features opposite.

These contain digestive enzymes. What kinds of stain will they remove and how will they do it?

Summary – Features of enzymes

1 They speed up chemical reactions without being changed.
2 Each enzyme speeds up only *one* type of reaction (e.g. pepsin only digests proteins).
3 Enzymes work best at a certain temperature (in humans that is 37°C).
4 Enzymes are destroyed by boiling.
5 Some enzymes work best in acid conditions (e.g. pepsin), some in neutral conditions and some in alkaline conditions.

Which of the enzymes on the right is an anabolic? Is the other one catabolic? If not what is it? Give reasons for your answers.

How enzymes work

One theory is that an enzyme has an 'active site' which combines briefly with a substance and changes it – splitting it apart, or linking two pieces together. The 'shape' of the active site fits only one type of molecule so it can control only one type of chemical reaction.

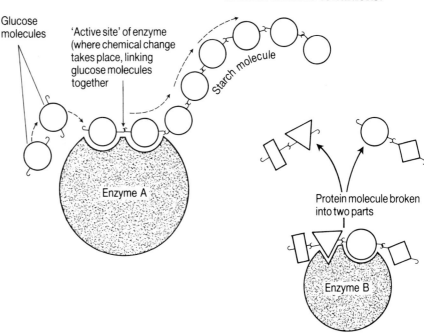

1·B Naming and classifying

The name robin is given to a type of thrush in North America, and a type of flycatcher in Australia.

Scientific names

Do you know what a *Taraxacum officinale* is? It's the scientific name for the dandelion plant. Every living thing known to science is given an official scientific name which is then used throughout the world.

Why do scientists invent names which are difficult to learn and say? Why aren't common names, like dandelion, good enough? Try to answer these questions yourself after reading the following.

1 Many creatures have more than one common name: they can have several different English names and many foreign language names if found abroad.

2 The same common name may be used for different animals (see photographs opposite).

3 Scientists have found over 1 500 000 different kinds of living thing, but only a few have a common name.

Think of reasons why scientific names are essential. Why, for instance, would using common names in scientific papers and lectures cause confusion?

Scientific names are essential for communication between scientists so that they can be sure they are all talking about the same thing, and for naming organisms which have no common name.

An American Elk. What we call an elk is called a moose by North Americans, and they use the name elk for what we call a red deer.

Classification

Classification is sorting living things into groups. This makes the task of studying the enormous variety of life far easier.

Horse, dog, bird and fish are groups of animals. If we did not have the word 'horse' what would you have to say when you wanted to tell someone about horses?

If there were no group names we would have to describe objects when talking about them. Instead of 'chair' we would have to say 'a thing with legs which you sit on'.

The smallest group of living things is called a **species**. Each dot on this diagram is a species.

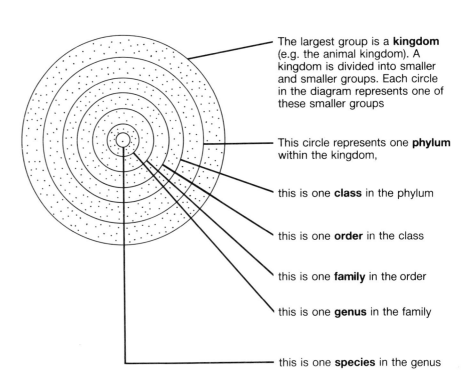

The largest group is a **kingdom** (e.g. the animal kingdom). A kingdom is divided into smaller and smaller groups. Each circle in the diagram represents one of these smaller groups

This circle represents one **phylum** within the kingdom,

this is one **class** in the phylum

this is one **order** in the class

this is one **family** in the order

this is one **genus** in the family

this is one **species** in the genus

How to classify living things

Living things are sorted into groups which share certain features. A kingdom contains a large number of organisms but they have few things in common. The **plant kingdom** contains thousands of species but they only share the ability to make food by photosynthesis.

The smaller the group the fewer species it contains, but the more features they share.

*Humans belong to a group called **primates**. It also includes monkeys and apes. From these pictures make a list of some features primates have in common. How are humans different from monkeys and apes?*

Species

A species is a group of living things which have so many features in common that they can mate together and produce young which are fertile (they can also mate and have young). See the photograph opposite. Humans, dogs, cats and sunflowers are all examples of species.

Every species is given two scientific names: the first one for its genus and the second one for its species. *Homo sapiens* is the scientific name for humans.

Horses and donkeys are different species but are so alike they can breed. But their young, called mules (above), are infertile.

More about keys

You can learn more about keys by making one for yourself.

Study the leaves illustrated below. List those features which make each leaf different from all the others. The table opposite will help you to do this.

Next, arrange these features together in pairs, like the key in Unit 1.3.

Features	A	B	C	D	E
Leaf made up of small leaflets					
Leaf edge with many teeth					
Leaf edge divided into large teeth					
Leaf veins parallel or branched					

1 *Recall knowledge*
Vocabulary test Write out the numbered phrases then, opposite each, write the word from the list of technical terms which the phrase describes.

respiration, excretion, photosynthesis, chlorophyll, vertebrates, invertebrates, antenna, spores, biosphere, phytoplankton, mammary glands, dicotyledons, marsupials, coelenterates

1 A green chemical in plant leaves
2 Removal of wastes from the body
3 Animals with backbones
4 Insect sense organs
5 Their leaves have a network of veins
6 The parts of our planet which can support life
7 How plants make food
8 They carry their young in a pouch
9 Jelly fish are examples
10 Getting energy from food
11 Mosses and ferns use them to reproduce
12 Animals without backbones
13 They produce milk
14 Microscopic plants

2 *Understanding*
In each of the following groups of living things find the one which is LEAST related to the other four.

Honey bee	Spider
Bat	Grasshopper
Sparrow	Housefly
Penguin	Butterfly
Flying fish	Ant
Lizard	Haddock
Frog	Mackerel
Alligator	Whale
Tortoise	Cod
Snake	Goldfish
Oyster	Iris
Octopus	Horsechestnut tree
Snail	Moss
Slug	Stinging nettle
Starfish	Buttercup

3 *Recall knowledge*
All living things *move, have senses, feed, respire, excrete, reproduce,* and *grow.*

Write out these seven features as headings across a page. Then sort the list below into seven groups under the headings.

fins	seeds
photosynthesis	eggs
kidneys	taste
babies	sunlight
energy	oxygen
muscles	lungs
eyes	mating
root growth	leaf-fall
leaves	seedlings

4 *Recall knowledge*
a) Write down three headings: *Animals only, Plants only* and *Both animals and plants.*
b) Now sort the list below into three groups under these headings.

excretion
photosynthesis
movement from place to place
growth throughout life
respiration
eating other living things
growth towards light
growth stops when adult size is reached

5 *Recall Knowledge*
Look at each statement below. Which animal or group of animals does it describe?
a) They have three pairs of legs.
b) They move about on a large slimy foot.
c) They have a thick, hard cuticle, and two pairs of antennae.
d) They have tentacles and a beak like a bird.
e) They carry their babies in a pouch.
f) The body is like a bag, with a mouth and tentacles at one end.

6 *Recall knowledge*
Look at each statement below. Which group of plants does it describe?
a) Spore capsules grow on the backs of their leaves.
b) Grasses, sycamore trees and tulips are examples.
c) Their seeds grow inside cones.

7 Interpret data

Solution X is a clear solution in water of substances A, B and C. One of these substances is an enzyme. **Solution Y** is a slightly cloudy, colourless liquid.

Information

a) When solutions X and Y are mixed and left in a warm place for a few minutes the mixture gives a negative reaction with a starch test (i.e. iodine does not produce a blue colour) but it gives a positive reaction with a glucose test (i.e. Fehlings solution goes brick red).

b) If weak acid is added to solution X substance C comes out of solution and settles to the bottom as a white powder (i.e. it is **precipitated**). If, after the precipitate is filtered out, the remaining liquid is added to solution Y and left for a few minutes the mixture gives a negative starch reaction and a positive glucose reaction. If the precipitate is put in water and added to solution Y and left for a few minutes, both starch and glucose tests are positive.

c) If solution X is boiled for a few minutes both B and C are precipitated. If these are filtered out and the remaining liquid added to solution Y and left for a few minutes it gives positive results with both starch and glucose tests. If the precipitate is put in water and added to solution Y and left for a few minutes it also gives a positive result with starch and glucose tests.

d) If a weak alkali is added to solution X both A and C are precipitated. If these are filtered out and the remaining liquid added to solution Y and left for a few minutes the mixture gives positive results with both starch and glucose tests. If the precipitates are put into water they redissolve. If this solution is added to solution Y and left for a few minutes, it gives a negative result with a starch test, and a positive result with a glucose test.

Questions

a) Which of the three substances is an enzyme?

b) What does the enzyme do?

c) Explain how you decided that the other two are not enzymes.

d) What can you say about the contents of solution Y?

8 Recall Knowledge

The drawings below show some living things. Which of them:

a) is a vertebrate?

b) is an invertebrate?

c) is a mammal?

d) is an insect?

e) makes food by photosynthesis?

f) lives by making things decay?

g) reproduces with seeds?

h) reproduces with spores?

i) suckles young on milk?

j) has compound eyes?

Bread mould fungus (×100)

Minnow

Grasshopper

Polypodium fern

Tulip flower

Slug

Field mouse

Moss (×10)

2·1 What are cells?

A house is built of bricks. In the same way, animals and plants are built of **cells**.

Your skin, your bones, your muscles, and your brain are all made of cells. There are around a hundred million million cells in your body. They are very tiny. At least ten cells would fit side by side across this next full-stop.

Inside an animal cell

Your cells are not very different from the cells of a frog or a cat or a giraffe. In fact all animal cells have these parts:

A cell from the lining of a human cheek, coloured to show up the different parts. What do you think the orange blob is?

A cell membrane. This is a thin skin around the cell. It lets some things pass through, but stops others.

Cytoplasm. This is a jelly containing hundreds of chemicals. Lots of chemical reactions go on in it. It fills the cell.

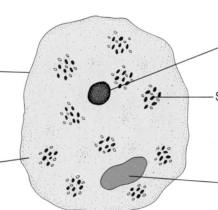

Stored food

A nucleus. It controls what a cell does, and how it develops.

A vacuole. This is a space within the cell containing air, liquids, or food particles. Animal cells usually have several small vacuoles.

Cells are not all the same shape. There are about twenty different types of cell in your body, all doing different jobs. Below are photographs of three types of cell.

Red blood cells are disc shaped. Their job is to carry oxygen round the body.

White blood cells, stained to show up clearly. They can change shape. They attack germs.

Nerve cells have long thin fibres which carry 'messages' around your body.

Inside a plant cell

All plant cells have these parts:

A cell wall of cellulose. It covers the cell membrane.

Cytoplasm.

Nucleus

Stored food. Mainly starch.

A vacuole. All plant cells have these. The liquid inside them is called **cell sap**.

Chloroplasts. These are tiny discs full of a green substance called **chlorophyll**. They trap the light energy that plants need for making food by photosynthesis.

Unlike animal cells, there are only a few different shapes of plant cells. This is because there are not so many different jobs for them to do.

Leaf cells. They look firmer than animal cells because of their cell walls. The tiny green blobs are chloroplasts. There are several in each cell.

A slice through a nettle stem. Some cells form tubes to carry water, others to carry foods.

How plant cells are different from animal cells

Plant cells	Animal cells
1 have cellulose cell walls	1 do not have cellulose cell walls
2 have chloroplasts	2 do not have chloroplasts
3 always have a vacuole	3 sometimes have a vacuole
4 have a few different shapes	4 have many different shapes

Questions

1 Name three different kinds of cell in your body.
2 What is cytoplasm?
3 What does a cell nucleus do?
4 What are chloroplasts. What do they contain?

What do they do?
5 How are plant cells different from animal cells? List four differences.
6 List four things found in *both* plant cells and animal cells.

2·2 How living things grow

You started life as a single cell – a fertilized egg cell. You grew because that cell divided to make two cells, these divided to make four, and so on. This is called **cell division**. It is how all living things grow.

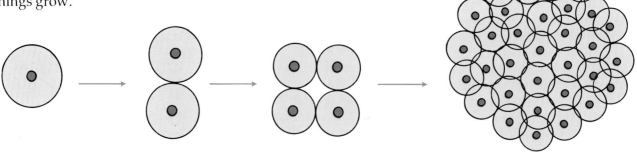

A fertilized egg cell divides to make *two* **daughter** cells, which are identical.

These divide to make *four* identical cells, which divide again and again to make a ball of cells.

Tissues

Some cells in the ball grow and change shape to do a particular job – they become **specialized**. Cells that do the same job group together to form **tissues**.

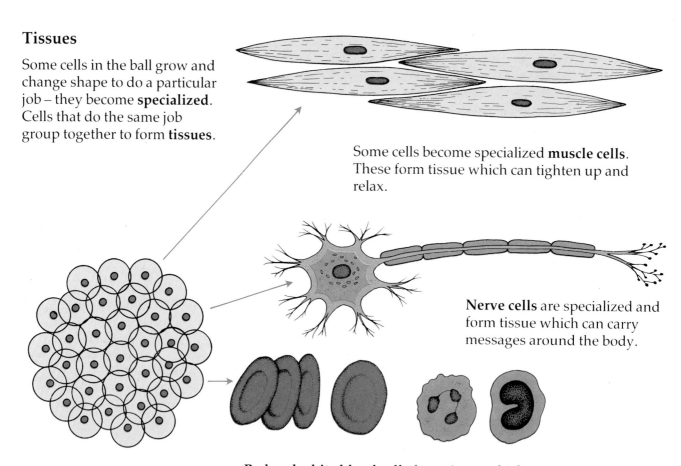

Some cells become specialized **muscle cells**. These form tissue which can tighten up and relax.

Nerve cells are specialized and form tissue which can carry messages around the body.

Red and white blood cells form tissue which can carry oxygen and kill germs. This tissue is called **blood**.

Organs

Different tissues combine to make **organs**.

The **heart** is an organ which pumps blood around the body.

The **stomach** is an organ which digests food.

The **brain** is an organ which controls parts of the body.

Organisms and organ systems

You are an **organism**. So is a cat and so is a bird. An organism is made up of many different organs. Some of its organs work together to form **organ systems**.

The **circulatory system** is made up of the heart and blood vessels.

The **digestive system** is made up of the gullet, stomach, and intestine.

The **nervous system** is made up of the brain, spinal cord, and nerves.

Questions

1 What is a tissue? Give two examples.
2 What is an organ? Give five examples.
3 What is an organ system? Give two examples.

4 Even when you are fully grown some cells carry on dividing. Explain why.
5 Explain what a specialized cell is.

2·3 In and out of cells

Substances pass in and out of cells as tiny particles called **molecules**.

Molecules are the smallest particles of a substance. The molecules in liquids and gases are never still. They keep moving and bumping into each other.

A glass of water **Water magnified millions of times**

Water molecules are always on the move

An experiment to show that molecules move

A drop of ink is added to water. The ink spreads through the water even though it is not stirred.

The ink spreads because ink molecules move into the spaces between water molecules, and water molecules move into the spaces between ink molecules.

Ink

Ink molecule

Diffusion of ink →
← Diffusion of water

The movement of molecules so that they mix is called **diffusion**. Molecules diffuse from where they are plentiful to where they are less plentiful.

Diffusion in and out of cells

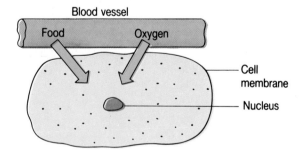

Blood vessel

Food   Oxygen

Cell membrane

Nucleus

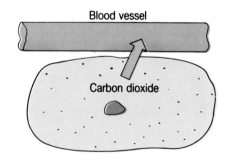

Blood vessel

Carbon dioxide

Human body cells need a constant supply of food and oxygen to stay alive and do their jobs. Food and oxygen are carried in the blood, so they diffuse from the blood into each cell.

As the cell uses food and energy it produces carbon dioxide as waste. This waste must be removed before it poisons the cell. Carbon dioxide diffuses from the cell into the blood which carries it away to the lungs to be breathed out of the body.

Osmosis

Osmosis is a special kind of diffusion. It happens when a membrane has tiny holes in it which let water molecules pass through but stop larger molecules, like sugar. A membrane like this is called **semi-permeable**. This experiment shows osmosis:

○ Sugar molecule

o Water molecule

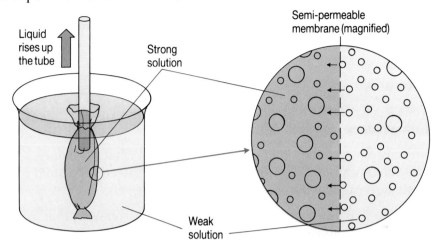

A semi-permeable membrane is tied to a tube. It is then filled with strong sugar solution.

The membrane is stood in a weak sugar solution. Soon liquid starts to rise up the tube.

The liquid rises because water molecules diffuse through the membrane from the weak solution to the strong one. But sugar molecules cannot diffuse like this because they are too big to pass through the membrane.

When a weak solution is separated from a strong one by a semi-permeable membrane, water always flows from the weak solution to the strong one. This diffusion of water is called **osmosis**.

Osmosis in plant cells

Water moves from cell to cell in plants by osmosis. The cell membrane of a plant cell is semi-permeable. So if a cell containing a weak solution is next to a cell with a stronger solution, water moves by osmosis from the weak to the strong solution, as shown in this diagram.

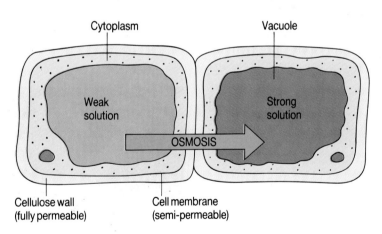

Questions

1 Why does ink move through water even without being stirred?

2 How does oxygen move from blood into body cells?

3 Osmosis is the movement of _____ from a _____ solution to a _____ solution through a _____ membrane.

4 What is a semi-permeable membrane?

2·4 Cell division

You started life as a fertilized egg cell, smaller than a full stop. You grew because this cell divided millions and millions of times to make new cells.

Chromosomes

When a cell is ready to divide, long thin threads called **chromosomes** appear in its nucleus.

Chromosomes contain chemicals which control what a cell does. These chemicals also contain all the instructions needed to build a whole new organism from a single fertilized egg cell.

When a cell divides it makes a new set of chromosomes so that these instructions can be passed to the daughter cells.

The chromosomes are always in pairs.

A cell dividing. The deep pink parts are the chromosomes.

How a cell divides

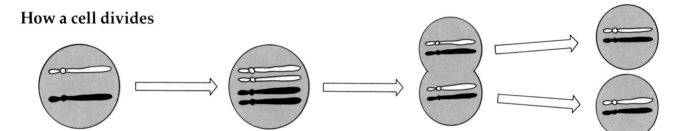

This cell has only two chromosomes. (Human cells have **46** chromosomes altogether.) Each chromosome splits into two, making a second set of chromosomes.

The *cell* divides in two. Each cell gets a *full set* of chromosomes. The two new cells have the same number of chromosomes as the first.

This kind of cell division is called **mitosis**. All the cells in animals and plants, *except* sex cells, are made by mitosis.

Mitosis produces:
1 the cells needed to make an adult organism from a fertilized egg
2 the cells needed to heal cuts, wounds, and broken bones
3 the cells that replace dead skin cells, and worn out red blood cells.

Mitosis produces the cells that let a seed grow into a plant.

Mitosis produces new bone cells which mend a broken arm.

How sex cells are produced

Some of the cells in your body are sex cells, or **gametes**. If you are male they are called **sperms** and are made in your **testes**. If you are female they are called **ova** or eggs, and are made in your **ovaries**. Sex cells are made by a different kind of cell division.

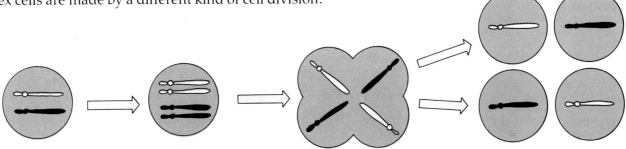

This cell is drawn to show only two chromosomes. Each chromosome splits into two, making a second set of chromosomes.

The cell divides to form *four* sex cells. Each sex cell gets only *half as many* chromosomes as the first cell. (Human sex cells have only **23** chromosomes.)

This kind of cell division is called **meiosis**. Meiosis produces sex cells in humans and other animals, and in plants.

Fertilization

At fertilization a male sex cell joins up with a female sex cell to make a fertilized egg cell called a **zygote**.

This drawing shows fertilization in humans.

In human fertilization a sperm with **23** chromosomes joins an ovum with **23** chromosomes to make a zygote with **46** chromosomes.

Fertilization happens in the same way in other animals, and in flowering plants. In flowering plants, the fertilized sex cell grows into a seed.

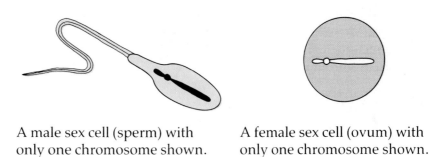

A male sex cell (sperm) with only one chromosome shown.

A female sex cell (ovum) with only one chromosome shown.

The sperm joins up with the ovum. This produces a zygote with the *full number of chromosomes*. This grows by mitosis into an adult.

Questions

1 Which kind of cell division:
   a) halves the chromosome number?
   b) produces cells to repair wounds?
   c) produces sperms?
   d) produces an adult from a zygote?

2 How are zygotes produced?

2·5 Heredity and variation

Heredity

You started life as a fertilized egg cell with 46 chromosomes. 23 of these chromosomes came from your father, and 23 from your mother. This is why you have some characteristics of your father and some of your mother.

All children inherit certain characteristics from their parents. The study of **inherited characteristics** is called **heredity**.

Hair colour

Hair type (straight, wavy, etc.)

Eye colour

Ear shape (lobed or unlobed)

Nose shape

Skin colour

Mouth shape

Inherited characteristics

The photograph above shows some of the characteristics children inherit from their parents. The development of these characteristics is controlled by chromosomes.

The children in the family below inherited some characteristics from each of their parents. Try to sort out which characteristic came from which parent.

Father has red curly hair, brown eyes, a snub nose, and a cleft chin.

Mother has straight black hair, blue eyes, a long thin nose, and a pointed chin.

Acquired characteristics

You may know how to swim, or rollerskate, or speak French. Or you may have a scar from a cut. These are **acquired characteristics**. You pick them up (acquire them) as you go through life. You are not born with them, and you cannot pass them on to your children.

Variation

No two people are exactly the same. Even identical twins are different in some ways.

People are different heights and weights. Their hair and eyes are different colours and their faces have different shapes. Their eye-colour and hair-colour show **variation**.

Continuous variations

These people are arranged in a line from the shortest to the tallest. Their height shows **continuous variation**. It varies from short to tall with many small differences in between.

Intelligence also shows continuous variation. Can you think of other variations which are continuous?

People's height shows continuous variation.

Discontinuous variation

People can either roll their tongues or they cannot. This is an example of **discontinuous variation**. You can either do it or you can't. There is no 'in between' state.

Blood groups show discontinuous variation. You belong to only one group: A, B, AB, or O. Find out what blood group each member of your class belongs to.

Can you think of any other variations that are discontinuous?

Tongue rolling. Either you can . . . or you can't.

Questions

1 Write down eight inherited characteristics.

2 Write down six acquired characteristics.

3 Intelligence shows continuous variation. What does this mean?

4 Colour blindness shows discontinuous variation. What does this mean?

5 Write down four of your own acquired characteristics.

2·6 Chromosomes and genes

You inherit characteristics from your parents through their chromosomes.

A chromosome has small parts called **genes** all the way along it. The genes are made of a chemical called **DNA**. Genes control the development of inherited characteristics. For example, there are genes which control eye colour, hair colour and skin colour.

What happens to genes during fertilization

A sperm has 23 chromosomes with genes from a man. An ovum (egg) has 23 chromosomes with genes from a woman. During fertilization the sperm and ovum join together.

Each chromosome from the sperm then pairs up with a matching chromosome from the ovum. This brings the two sets of genes together. The genes for hair colour pair up, the genes for skin colour pair up, and so on. *Genes always work in pairs.*

The genes in a pair may be identical. For example, they may both produce black hair. But if one is a gene for black hair and the other a gene for blond hair they are in competition.

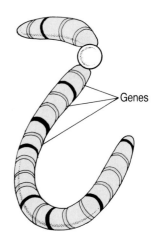

Genes

This is what a chromosome would look like if you could see the genes.

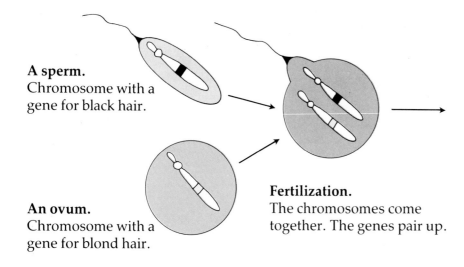

A sperm.
Chromosome with a gene for black hair.

An ovum.
Chromosome with a gene for blond hair.

Fertilization.
The chromosomes come together. The genes pair up.

The child has black hair. Only the gene for black hair has worked.

Dominant and recessive genes

The child has black hair because the gene for black hair is more powerful than the gene for blond hair. It **dominates** the gene for blond hair and produces the final hair colour. Genes which dominate other genes are called **dominant genes.**
Genes which are dominated are called **recessive genes.** When a dominant gene pairs up with a recessive gene, the dominant one produces the final effect.

Genes in action

In diagrams, genes are usually shown by letters. Capital letters are used for dominant genes and small letters for recessive genes. In the diagram below, H is the gene for black hair and h is the gene for blond hair.

Mother's cells contain two genes for black hair (HH) so she has black hair.

Father's cells contain two genes for blond hair (hh) so he has blond hair.

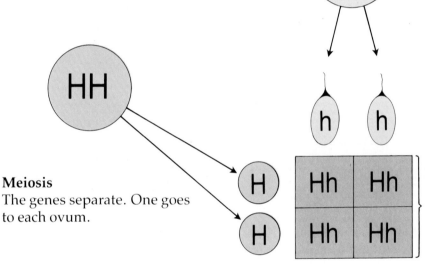

Meiosis
The genes separate. One goes to each ovum.

Meiosis
The genes separate. One goes to each sperm.

Zygotes
All have the genes Hh. So all the children will have black hair, because the gene for black hair is dominant.

Homozygous and heterozygous

A person with two identical genes for a characteristic is pure bred or **homozygous** for that characteristic. (HH is a pure bred gene.) A person with two different genes (one dominant and one recessive) for a characteristic is **hybrid** or **heterozygous** for that characteristic. (**Homo** means the same and **hetero** means different.)

Questions

1 Which parts of chromosomes control inherited characteristics?

2 What are genes made of?

3 In the gene pair Hh (for black and blond hair) which gene is dominant?

4 If E is the gene for brown eyes, and e is the gene for blue eyes, what eye colour will the following gene pairs give?
a) EE **b)** Ee **c)** ee

5 Look at question 4 and pick out a gene pair which is heterozygous, and a gene pair which is homozygous.

2·7 More about chromosomes

On the previous page all the children had dark hair, even though their father was blond. This happened because they inherited a dominant gene (H) and a recessive gene (h). They were **hybrids**, or **heterozygous** (Hh) for hair colour.

This does not mean that blond hair has been lost altogether. Look what happens when two hybrids have children.

Mother's cells have the genes Hh so she has black hair.

↓

Meiosis produces two types of ovum.

Father's cells have the genes Hh so he has black hair.

↓

Meiosis produces two types of sperm.

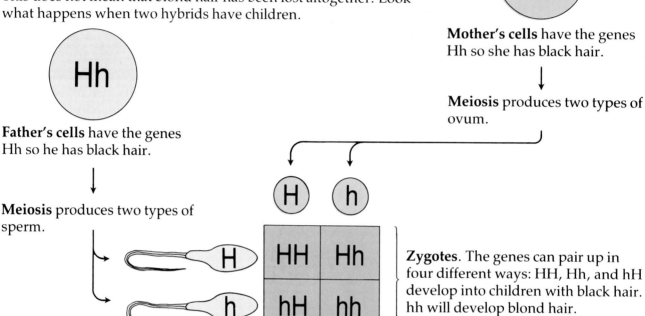

Zygotes. The genes can pair up in four different ways: HH, Hh, and hH develop into children with black hair. hh will develop blond hair.

Blond hair appears this time because two recessive genes (hh) can come together. But the children are three times more likely to have black hair than blond hair.

Other dominant characteristics

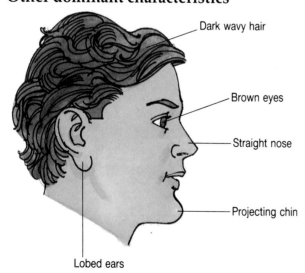

Dark wavy hair

Brown eyes

Straight nose

Projecting chin

Lobed ears

Other recessive characteristics

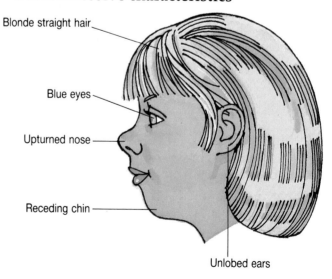

Blonde straight hair

Blue eyes

Upturned nose

Receding chin

Unlobed ears

Boy or girl?

Human cells have 46 chromosomes altogether. There are 22 matching pairs. But the last pair does not always match. These two chromosomes are the **sex chromosomes**. They control whether a baby develops into a boy or a girl.

If you are male your cells have an X chromosome, and a smaller Y chromosome. If you are female your cells have two X chromosomes. This diagram shows how sex is inherited.

Mother's cells contain two X chromosomes.

↓

Meiosis produces ova with one X chromosome each.

Father's cells contain an X and a Y chromosome.

↓

Meiosis produces equal numbers of X and Y sperms.

XY zygotes develop into boys.

XX zygotes develop into girls.

Since there are equal numbers of X and Y sperms a child has an equal chance of being a boy or a girl.

This picture shows the 46 chromosomes of a man. They were photographed under a microscope, then cut out and sorted into 22 matching pairs, and a pair of X and Y chromosomes.

Questions

1 W is the gene for wavy hair, and w is the gene for straight hair. Father has the genes WW. Mother has the genes Ww. Draw a diagram like the one on the previous page to show what type of hair their children could inherit.

2 What do XY zygotes develop into? What do XX zygotes develop into?

3 Why are there roughly equal numbers of boys and girls?

2·8 More about genes

Alleles

Some people have brown eyes. Some have blue eyes or green eyes. Each eye colour is controlled by a different gene.

All the different genes which control a characteristic are called the **alleles** of that characteristic. So the genes for brown, blue, and green eyes are the alleles for eye colour.

Phenotype and genotype

A **phenotype** is a characteristic you can see, such as black hair, an up-turned nose, or the colour of a flower.

A **genotype** is the set of genes which produce a phenotype.

Genotype also means the complete set of genes in an organism. So your genotype is the complete set of genes which made a zygote turn into you.

Flower colour is a phenotype produced by the genotype CC or Cc. White flowers (flowers with *no* colour) have the genotype cc.

Black hair is a phenotype produced by the genotype HH or Hh. Blond hair is a phenotype produced by the genotype hh.

Genes and the environment

Organisms with the same genotype should look the same. But they may look different if they grow in different surroundings or **environments.** The environment can affect the way genes work.

These maize plants have the same genotype. But they look different because they were grown in different soils.

The ones captioned 'Complete' were grown in soil that had everything they needed. The ones captioned 'No nitrogen' were grown in soil that had everything *except* nitrogen. So the different soils have given different phenotypes from the same genotype.

Complete nutrients.

No nitrogen.

Mutations

A **mutation** is a sudden change in a gene or chromosome. A mutation changes the way an organism develops.

A gene mutation can cause extra fingers and toes to grow. This does not happen very often.

A chromosome mutation can cause a woman to produce an ovum with 24 chromosomes instead of 23. If it gets fertilized the baby has 47 chromosomes instead of 46, and develops **Down's syndrome**. About 1 in 700 babies are affected.

What causes mutations?

Mutations can occur naturally. They can also be caused by x-rays, other radiation, and by some chemicals.

The fruitfly on the left was exposed to gamma radiation, which caused a gene mutation. As a result, its offspring (on the right) has crumpled wings.

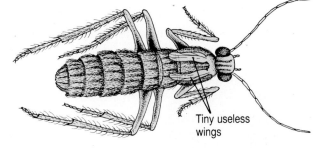

Tiny useless wings

A flightless moth from the Island of Kerguelen in the Indian Ocean. Tiny, useless wings are caused by a gene mutation. Usually the insects don't live as long as their winged brothers and sisters. But Kerguelan is very windy, and the winged insects get blown out to sea. Crawling, flightless insects are safe.

Questions

1   In fruit flies, R gives red eyes and r gives white eyes. What is the phenotype of these genotypes:
    a) RR?   b) Rr?   c) rr?

2   In mice, B gives dark hair and b gives light hair. What are the genotypes for dark-haired mice?

3   What is a mutation? What causes mutations?

4   Describe a harmful mutation, and a helpful mutation.

43

2·9 Evolution

Where have the millions of different living things come from? The most likely answer is that they were produced by **evolution.**

What is evolution?

Evolution means change and improvement from simple beginnings. Modern aircraft were evolved by changing and improving the first simple aircraft designs.

Evolution of living things

The first living things appeared about 3500 million years ago. They were no more than bubbles full of chemicals but they could reproduce.

Some of the young were different from their parents. Some of the differences meant they could survive better than their parents. Over billions of years, these changes and improvements led to all the different creatures alive today.

The first powered aircraft evolved to become Concorde.

This diagram shows how vertebrates could have evolved from simple beginnings.

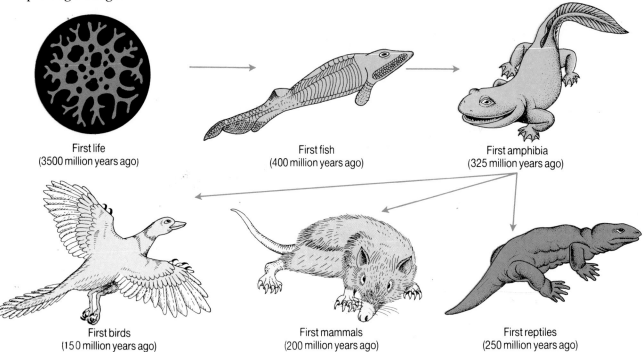

First life
(3500 million years ago)

First fish
(400 million years ago)

First amphibia
(325 million years ago)

First birds
(150 million years ago)

First mammals
(200 million years ago)

First reptiles
(250 million years ago)

Natural selection

Living things are at risk from disease, predators, and other dangers. If the young are born with differences that make them tougher, or stronger, or better suited to their surroundings, they will be able to live longer and have more babies than their weaker brothers and sisters.

This idea is called **survival of the fittest,** or **natural selection**. Nature *selects* the fittest and strongest for survival by killing off the weaklings. The idea was first put forward by Charles Darwin about a hundred years ago.

Darwin suggested that the young inherit improvements from their parents. In this way a species could keep on improving until it produced a new species.

Can you spot the pale Peppered moth? Here its colouring helps to protect it from enemies.

These photographs show an example of natural selection.

They show dark and light varieties of the Peppered moth. In soot-blackened city areas the light ones are easily seen and eaten by birds, so the dark ones are common. But in clean country areas the dark ones are easily found by birds, so that light ones are more common.

The dark Peppered moth is safer resting on dark surfaces, like this sooty tree trunk . . .

. . . but a pale Peppered moth on a dark surface is easily spotted by birds.

Artificial selection

Animal and plant breeders have proved that selection can change a species. They use the **artificial selection** process.

They select and breed sheep with the longest coats, pigs with the most meat, trees with the juiciest fruit, and plants with the most colourful flowers. So we now have thousands of plants and animals that are very different from their wild ancestors.

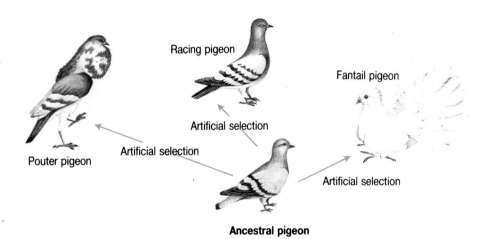

All these different pigeons were produced by artifical selection.

Questions

1 What does evolution mean?
2 What does natural selection mean?
3 How does natural selection make dark Peppered moths more common near factories than light ones.

4 Explain how one species may produce a new species over millions of years.
5 What does artificial selection mean?
6 Give one example of artificial selection.

2 C ells

Cell size

Cells are called the building-blocks out of which living things are made, because they are a bit like the bricks which make up a wall.

But bricks are dead, all the same shape and large, whereas cells are alive, have many different shapes and are microscopic in size. Your body contains about 100 million million cells, and they measure between 0.005 mm and 0.02 mm across. This doesn't make you much wiser about cell size, so find out more for yourself:

1   *Pull out one hair from your head, put it on white paper and place a millimetre ruler on top. About 10 hairs side-by-side measure 1 mm.*
2   *The drawing opposite compares the diameter of a hair with a number of different cells.*
3   *Microscopic things are measured in **micrometres**. One micrometre is one thousandth of a millimetre and is written $1\mu m$.*
4   *The hair in the drawing is divided into strips $10\mu m$ wide.*
5   *Estimate the diameter in micrometres of cheek cells, and red blood cells.*
6   *About how many red blood cells side-by-side would equal the diameter of a hair?*
7   *Measure the diameter of a tennis ball. How many times would you have to enlarge a human cheek cell to make it the same diameter? How tall would you be if you were enlarged by the same amount?*

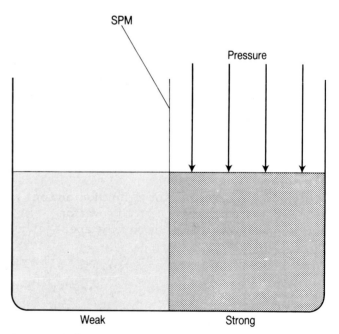

Cells and osmosis

Unit 2.3 explains that osmosis is the movement of water through a semi-permeable membrane from a weak to a strong solution.

As a cell takes in water by osmosis what will happen to the concentration of its cell sap, and the rate at which water enters by osmosis?

The rate at which water enters a cell by osmosis depends on the amount of dissolved material in its sap, i.e. the *strength* of this solution. The stronger this solution compared with liquid outside the cell the faster the rate of osmosis or, put another way, the greater the *pressure* of water trying to enter the cell. Study the diagram opposite before reading on.

Osmotic pressure.   This is the pressure required to stop osmosis. At this pressure water is squeezed back through a semi-permeable membrane as fast as it enters by osmosis.

Water will flow by osmosis from the weak solution on the left through the semi-permeable membrane (SPM) into the strong solution. What would happen to this flow if you could exert pressure on the strong solution? Explain your answer.

All living cells are surrounded by a semi-permeable **cell membrane**, but in plant cells this is surrounded by a thick **cellulose cell wall** (Unit 2.1). Cellulose is freely permeable to all liquids but it stretches very little. Study the diagram below.

Cell turgidity. A cell taking in water by osmosis swells because its contents press outwards against the cell wall. Plant cells expand until their cellulose walls can stretch no further, or until pressure from surrounding cells stops them expanding. The cells are now firm, like pumped-up footballs, and are said to be **fully turgid**. The stretched cellulose wall and surrounding cells exerts an inward pressure which eventually equals the osmotic pressure of the cell sap, so osmosis stops.

Animal cells have no cellulose wall and so expand much further when taking in water by osmosis. They don't burst because they also are surrounded by expanding cells which press against each other with ever increasing force until further expansion is impossible.

Osmoregulation. There is another reason why the cells of some animals are unlikely to take in water and burst. Kidneys control the osmotic pressure of liquid surrounding their cells by continually adjusting the quantity of dissolved material. So, the liquid never becomes so weak that cells are damaged. This process is called **osmoregulation**.

Plasmolysis. A cell surrounded by liquid stronger than its cell sap will lose water by osmosis. The cell shrinks and becomes soft or **flaccid**. In plants the cell membrane usually pulls away from the cellulose cell wall (see diagram opposite). These effects on cells are called **plasmolysis**.

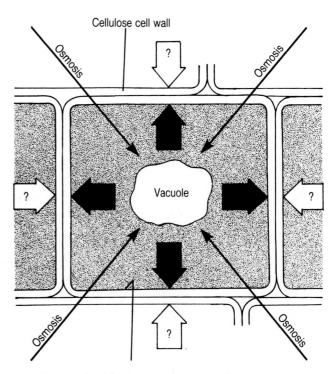

As a cell takes in water by osmosis it expands. When will a plant cell stop expanding? (What inward force is represented by the white arrows?) Will osmosis stop at this point? Explain your answer. What could stop animal cells, which have no cellulose wall, inflating until they burst?

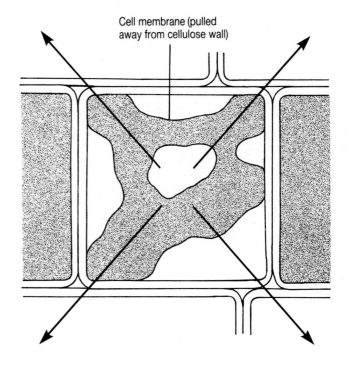

Cell shape

The shape of a cell depends on its function, and on pressure from surrounding cells. Discover for yourself the effects of pressure on cell shape.

1   Make some small Plasticine balls. Completely surround one ball with others of the same size then roll them all between your hands until they are squashed firmly together. Pull them carefully apart and look at the different shapes, especially the centre ball.

2   Arrange six Plasticine rods around a central one and roll them on a desk top to squash them together. Pull them apart and look at their shape. Study the slice through a nettle stem in Unit 2.1. Which cells could your Plasticine shapes represent?

1 *Recall knowledge*
Vocabulary test Write out the numbered phrases below then, opposite each, write the word from the list of technical terms which the phrase describes.

nucleus, vacuole, cytoplasm, tissue, organ, osmosis, chromosome, fertilization, gametes, zygote, genes, homozygous, heterozygous, mitosis, meiosis, genotype, phenotype, mutation

1 A sudden change in a chromosome or gene

2 A gene pair, the members of which are different (i.e. one dominant and one recessive)

3 The visible, as opposed to the genetic, characteristics of an organism

4 A group of cells specialized to do a particular job

5 Movement of water through a semi-permeable membrane from a weak to a strong solution

6 A space in a cell usually filled with liquid

7 It happens when a sperm and ovum come together

8 Made up of several different tissues

9 A gene pair, the members of which are identical

10 When a cell divides and produces two cells with a full set of chromosomes

11 All of a cell except the nucleus

12 The part of a cell which contains chromosomes

13 They control the development of inherited characteristics (e.g. eye colour)

14 Sperms and ova

15 Made up of many different genes

16 A name for the full set of genes possessed by an organism

17 A fertilized egg cell

18 When a cell divides and produces two cells with half the normal number of chromosomes

2 *Interpret data and design*
An uncooked potato was peeled. A piece from the middle was cut into two strips X and Y, each 50 mm long. One strip was placed in a strong sugar solution. Another strip was placed in pure water.

Liquid (water or strong sugar solution)

Potato strip

After 30 minutes strip X had grown longer. Strip Y had shrunk.
   a) What could have happened to the cells in each strip, to make one strip swell and the other shrink?
   b) Which strip had been placed in the sugar solution? Explain your answer.
   c) The experiment was repeated using strips of cooked potato. These strips did not change in length. Can you explain why?
   d) If you had some sugar solution which was exactly the same osmotic pressure (see page 46) as a potato cell and you placed a potato strip in it how, if at all, would it change?
   e) Design an experiment using potato strips to produce a sugar solution with the same osmotic pressure as a potato cell. List your apparatus, and describe your method in full detail.

3 *Recall knowledge*
   a) What is a tissue? Name two examples.
   b) What is an organ? Name two examples.
   c) What is an organ system? Name the organ system which:
   carries 'messages' around the body;
   changes food into a liquid;
   carries food, oxygen and wastes around the body.

4 *Interpret data*

The diagram below shows how wing shape is inherited in fruit flies. W is the gene for normal wings and w is the gene for curly wings. Flies 1, 2, 7 and 8 are homozygous.

a) What are the genotypes of flies 3, 4, 9 and 10?

b) What do their phenotypes tell you about the effects of the environment on the inheritance of wing shape.

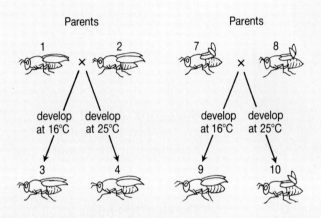

5 *Interpret data*

a) A strong sugar solution was poured into a bag made of semi-permeable membrane.

b) The bag was placed in a beaker of water (diagram A below).

c) After about half an hour it looked like diagram B.

d) Explain why the bag changed shape in this way.

e) What would happen if the bag was placed in a stronger sugar solution than the solution inside it?

6 *Identify a problem and formulate hypotheses*

A family noticed that their pet cat was infested with fleas. They dusted it once with insecticide powder and almost every flea was killed.

A few months later the cat was again badly infested with fleas. They had to dust it several times, using insecticide from the same tin, in order to kill most of the fleas.

A few weeks later the cat was again badly infested with fleas. This time dusting with powder from the same tin had very little effect on the fleas.

a) Identify a problem which arises from these observations.

b) Suggest as many hypotheses as you can to explain what is happening. At least one hypothesis should be based on the information given on p.43 of unit 2.8. Other hypotheses need have nothing to do with genetics.

7 *Interpret data*

a) E is the gene for brown eye colour, and e is the gene for blue eye colour. Which gene is dominant?

b) Both father and mother have the genes Ee in their cells. What colour are their eyes?

c) Copy the diagram below. Complete it to show how the genes in each sex cell come together at fertilization.

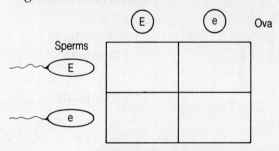

d) Which of the fertilized cells (zygotes) are homozygous for eye colour? Which are heterozygous?

e) Which zygotes will produce children with blue eyes? Which will produce children with brown eyes?

f) Complete the diagram again but this time with a father whose eye-colour genes are EE, and with a mother whose eye-colour genes are Ee. How does this affect the chance that they will have a blue-eyed or a brown-eyed child?

3·1 Flowering plants

FLOWERING PLANTS

There are thousands of plants that flower. Daisies, tomato plants, grasses, and chestnut trees are just some of them. Can you think of others? Flowers have male and female **sex organs**. These make **seeds** from which new plants grow.

The parts of a flowering plant

The **flower** contains the male and female sex organs. These make seeds.

The **leaves** make food for the plant by photosynthesis. For this they need sunlight, carbon dioxide from the air, and water and minerals from the soil.

Roots anchor a plant in the soil. They also take in water and minerals from it.

Most of the water and minerals are taken in through the **root hairs**.

Buds contain small, partly-grown, leaves or flowers. The buds protect these young parts.

The **stem** has tubes inside it. Some tubes carry water and minerals from the roots to the leaves. Other tubes carry food up and down the plant.

Soil level

This is a **main root**.

This is a **side root**, or **lateral root**.

Which flowering plant is this?

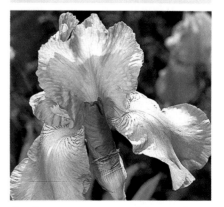

And can you name this one?

50

How plants make food

Plants make food by **photosynthesis**. Photosynthesis means making things with light. That is what plants do. They use light energy to make food from carbon dioxide and water.

Inside a leaf is a green substance called **chlorophyll**. It can trap energy from sunlight.

Carbon dioxide is taken into the leaf through tiny holes. Water is carried into the leaf from the stem through tubes.

Trapped light energy makes the carbon dioxide and water combine, to make a sugar called glucose, and oxygen. Glucose is used for food. Oxygen is given off into the air and keeps air breathable for all living things.

At night, photosynthesis stops.

Sun

LIGHT ENERGY

Carbon dioxide is taken from the air

Chlorophyll

Oxygen is given out

Glucose made in the leaves is taken to all parts of the plant

Water and minerals are taken in from the soil by the plant's roots

Here is a short way to show what happens during photosynthesis:

$$\text{water} + \text{carbon dioxide} \xrightarrow[\text{chlorophyll}]{\text{sunlight}} \text{glucose} + \text{oxygen}$$

How plants use the glucose from photosynthesis

1 Some is used straight away, to give the plant energy.
2 Some is stored up. It is changed into starch or oil, and stored in stems, roots, seeds, and fruits. When it is needed it is changed back to glucose.
3 Some is used to make cellulose for cell walls.
4 Some is combined with minerals, and used to make proteins and the other things plants need for growth.

Food factories – busy making food for a horsechestnut tree.

Questions

1 Where are the sex organs in a flowering plant?
2 What two things do roots do?
3 What is photosynthesis and where does it occur?
4 What is the green substance in leaves called?

5 What does this green substance do?
6 What does a plant need to make glucose?
7 What does a plant use the glucose for?
8 How is the glucose stored?
9 What else is produced during photosynthesis?

3·2 Leaves

Most leaves are thin and flat, like this:

These are **veins**.

This is the **mid-rib** of the leaf.

The stalk of a leaf is called a **petiole**.

The mid-rib and veins in this leaf are made of tiny tubes. Some of these tubes carry water and minerals into the leaf. Some carry food out to all parts of the plant.

Inside a leaf

This is what a slice of leaf looks like under a microscope.

The **upper skin** of the leaf. It has a layer of wax on it called a **cuticle**. This makes the leaf waterproof.

This thick layer of cells in the middle of a leaf makes glucose by **photosynthesis**.

Upper cuticle

Chloroplasts. These are tiny discs inside cells that contain **chlorophyll**. They trap light energy for photosynthesis.

Lower cuticle

This is another view of a piece of leaf.

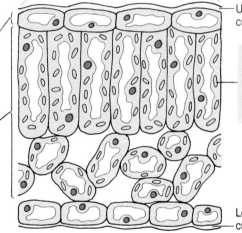

The tiny tubes in a **vein**. Some carry water and minerals into the leaf. Some carry food out.

Upper skin

Chloroplasts

Vein

Tiny hole in a leaf called a **stoma**.

Stomata

In most leaves, the lower skin has tiny holes in it called **stomata**. (One hole is called a **stoma**.) Stomata allow carbon dioxide to pass into the leaf, and oxygen and water vapour to pass out.

Stomata

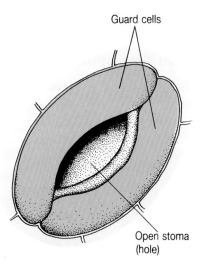

Guard cells

Open stoma (hole)

This is what the lower skin of a leaf looks like under a microscope.

This is one stoma, greatly magnified. It is opened and closed by the guard cells (described in unit 3.4).

How leaves are suited to photosynthesis

1 Many leaves are broad and flat, to absorb as much light as they can.
2 They are thin so carbon dioxide can reach inner cells easily.
3 They have plenty of stomata in the lower skin, to let carbon dioxide in, and oxygen and water vapour out.
4 They have plenty of veins to carry water to the photosynthesizing cells, and carry glucose away.

Dicotyledons, like this rhubarb, have broad leaves with a network of veins.

Monocotyledons, like this grass, have long narrow leaves with parallel veins.

Two stomata on a leaf, magnified by 8000. The top one is open, the bottom one closed.

Questions

1 What makes a leaf waterproof?
2 What are chloroplasts? Where are they found?
3 What is inside a leaf vein?

4 What are stomata? How do they help leaves make food?
5 Explain why leaves are thin and flat, and well-supplied with veins.

3·3 Transport and support in plants

A plant's transport system

A plant has lots of thin tubes inside it. They carry liquids up and down the plant. They are the plant's **transport system**.

Some tubes carry glucose solution from the leaves to every part of the plant. These tubes are called **phloem**.

Some tubes carry water and minerals up from the soil. They are called **xylem vessels**.

Xylem and phloem are grouped together in **vascular bundles**.

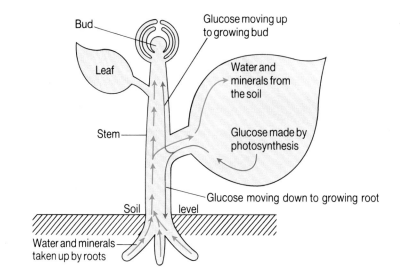

Bud

Leaf

Stem

Glucose moving up to growing bud

Water and minerals from the soil

Glucose made by photosynthesis

Glucose moving down to growing root

Soil level

Water and minerals taken up by roots

Inside a stem

This is what a thin slice of stem would look like, greatly magnified.

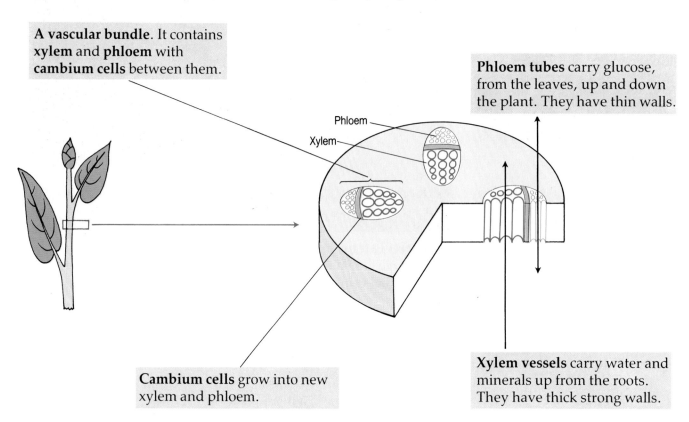

A vascular bundle. It contains **xylem** and **phloem** with **cambium cells** between them.

Phloem

Xylem

Phloem tubes carry glucose, from the leaves, up and down the plant. They have thin walls.

Cambium cells grow into new xylem and phloem.

Xylem vessels carry water and minerals up from the roots. They have thick strong walls.

Inside a root

This is what the tip of a root would look like, sliced open and greatly magnified.

Water and minerals flow up the **xylem vessels** to the stem.

Glucose from the leaves flows down the **phloem tubes**. It feeds the growing cells at the root tip.

Root hairs take in water and minerals from the soil.

Growing cells at the root tip.

The growing tip of the root is protected by a layer of cells called the **root cap**.

Support in plants

Xylem vessels have thick strong walls. So they help to hold up or support a plant. Bushes and trees have plenty of xylem to support them. In fact, tree trunks are mostly made of xylem.

The soft parts of plants, like leaves and flowers, are supported mainly by the water in their cells.

A plant with plenty of water has firm or **turgid** cells. Its stem is straight and its leaves and petals are firm.

A plant without water has soft or **flaccid** cells. Its stem, leaves and petals are soft. They droop, or **wilt.**

A white mustard seedling. It takes in water and minerals through its tiny root hairs.

Questions

1 a) Which tubes in a plant carry glucose?
   b) Where do they carry the glucose from?
   c) Where do they carry it to?

2 a) Which tubes carry water and minerals?
   b) Where do they carry them from?
   c) Where do they carry them to?

3 What does a vascular bundle contain?

4 Which cells grow into xylem and phloem?

5 Xylem vessels help support a plant. Why are they able to do this?

6 What is:
   a) a turgid cell?
   b) a flaccid cell?
   c) a root hair?

3·4 Transpiration

A plant loses water vapour through its leaves. This loss of water is called **transpiration**. The water first evaporates from cells inside a leaf. It then escapes through tiny holes in the leaf called stomata (one hole is called a stoma). In most plants stomata are on the undersides of the leaves.

The transpiration stream

Water is lost from the plant's leaves. At the same time more water flows up xylem vessels from the roots to replace it. This flow of water from roots to leaves is called the **transpiration stream**.

The transpiration stream flows fastest on warm dry sunny days, because this is when water evaporates fastest from the leaves. It slows down on cold, dull, damp, days and when a plant is short of water.

Some water is used for photosynthesis, and some evaporates from the leaves.

Water flows up the stem.

Water is taken in by plant roots.

How stoma work

A stoma is a hole between a pair of **guard cells**.

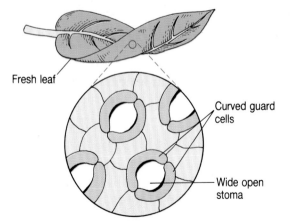

Fresh leaf

Curved guard cells

Wide open stoma

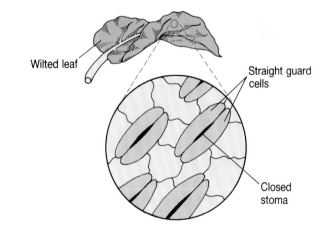

Wilted leaf

Straight guard cells

Closed stoma

When a plant has plenty of water, the guard cells become curved and the stoma between them opens. This allows water to escape from the leaves of the plant.

When a plant begins to lose water faster than its roots can take it up, guard cells become less curved. This closes the stomata and slows down the loss of water from the plant.

Why transpiration is important

1 The transpiration stream carries water and minerals from the soil to the leaves. Water is needed for photosynthesis. Minerals are needed for making proteins.

2 Water is also needed to keep cells turgid (firm), so that they support the plant (unit 3.3).

3 The evaporation of water from the leaves keeps them cool in hot weather.

How the transpiration stream flows

1 Root hairs take in water from the soil by osmosis (unit 2.3).

2 Water passes into the root. It moves from cell to cell until it reaches the xylem vessels.

3 Water is sucked up the vessels (like lemonade sucked up a drinking straw). Water passes into the leaves through leaf veins. Water evaporates from leaf cells and escapes through stomata.

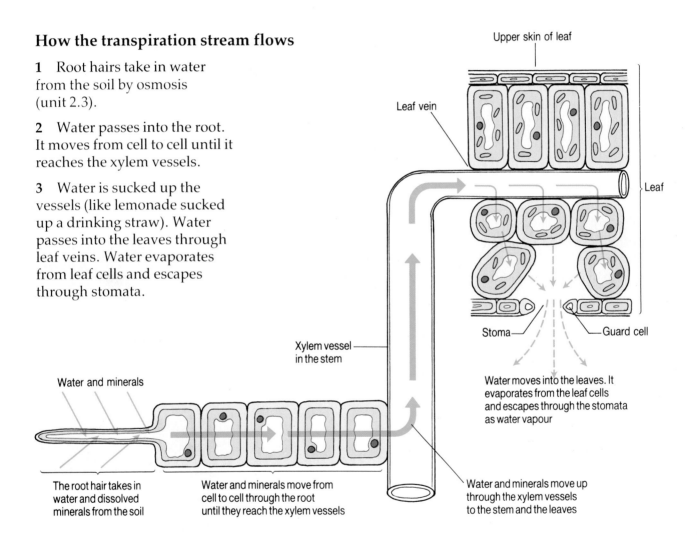

Upper skin of leaf

Leaf vein

Leaf

Stoma

Guard cell

Water moves into the leaves. It evaporates from the leaf cells and escapes through the stomata as water vapour

Xylem vessel in the stem

Water and minerals

The root hair takes in water and dissolved minerals from the soil

Water and minerals move from cell to cell through the root until they reach the xylem vessels

Water and minerals move up through the xylem vessels to the stem and the leaves

Questions

1 Does all the water which rises up a plant escape through the leaves?

2 **a)** What is the transpiration stream?
   b) Give three reasons why it is important.

3 When is the transpiration stream fastest?

4 What happens if water is lost from the leaves faster than it is taken up through the roots?

5 Explain how guard cells work.

3·5 Flowers

Humans have male and female sex organs, and so do flowering plants. A plant's sex organs are in its flowers. If you slice a flower open you will see something like this:

This is a male sex organ. It is called a **stamen**.

This is a swelling called a **nectary**. It makes **nectar**, a sweet liquid that attracts insects.

This is a **petal.** Some petals are coloured and scented to attract insects. Insects help plants to make seeds, as you will see later.

This is a female sex organ. It is called a **carpel**.

This is a **sepal**. Sepals protect the flower when it is in bud.

Parts of a stamen

The **anther**. It is made up of four **pollen sacs**. These are full of **pollen grains**. Pollen grains contain the male sex cells of the plant.

The stalk or **filament** of the stamen.

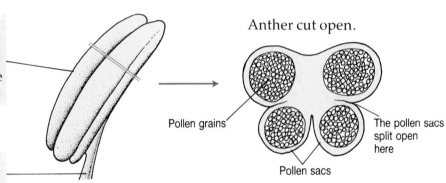

Anther cut open.

Pollen grains

The pollen sacs split open here

Pollen sacs

Parts of a carpel

The **stigma**. Pollen grains stick to this during pollination.

The **style**.

The **ovule** contains the female sex cell. It forms a seed after fertilization.

The **ovary** protects the ovule.

The **female sex cell**.

A tulip carpel surrounded by brown stamens. Note the large stigma at the top of the carpel. Why does it need to be sticky?

Some different flowers

There are many different kinds and shapes of flowers. They have different numbers of petals, stamens, and carpels. Some flowers, such as grasses, do not have any petals or nectaries.

The petals on a plum flower are all the same shape. Note the stamens sticking out. The stamens have long filaments with the anthers at the end.

A grass flower doesn't have petals, scent, or nectar. You can see it has very large anthers.

Sunflowers are made up of hundreds of small flowers, called florets, gathered together.

The petals on a pea-flower are of different shapes and sizes.

Questions

1 Why are some petals coloured and scented?
2 What is the name of:
   a) the male sex organ of a flowering plant?
   b) the female sex organ of a flowering plant?
3 What do sepals do?
4 What is nectar? Where is it made?

5 Copy and complete:
   The _____ is made up of four pollen _____ .
   These are full of _____ .
6 What is inside a pollen grain?
7 Draw a carpel and label the parts.
8 Draw a stamen and label the parts.

3·6 How fruits and seeds begin

A new seed begins when the male sex cell in a **pollen grain** joins up with a female sex cell in an **ovule**. The first step in making this happen is called **pollination**. Pollination takes place when pollen is carried from an anther to a stigma.

First the anther ripens. The pollen sacs split open releasing pollen grains.

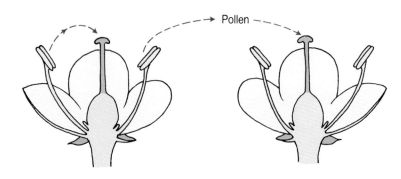

Pollen may be carried to a stigma in the *same* flower. This is called **self-pollination**.

Or pollen may be carried to a stigma in another flower. This is called **cross-pollination**.

Pollination by insects

Bees and other insects can carry pollen from flower to flower. That is what happens with buttercups, dandelions, and foxgloves.

Insect-pollinated flowers have:
1 large, coloured, scented petals and nectar, to attract insects
2 large pollen grains that can stick to an insect's body
3 anthers and stigmas inside the flower, so that the insect can brush against them when it is drinking nectar.

A bee with foxglove pollen clinging to its body. Inside this foxglove, the pollen will rub off on the sticky stigma.

60

Pollination by wind

The wind can carry pollen from flower to flower. That is what happens with grass, stinging nettle, and catkins.

Grass flowers

In catkins, the male and female sex organs are in separate flowers. Wind shakes the yellow pollen from the male catkin...

Wind-pollinated flowers do not have large scented petals, or nectar, because they do not need to attract insects.

They do have:
1 anthers that hang outside the flower, to catch the wind
2 large amounts of light, small pollen grains that blow in the wind
3 spreading, feathery stigmas to catch air-borne pollen grains.

...and carries it to the female catkin's sticky stigmas.

Fertilization

After a pollen grain lands on a stigma the next step is **fertilization**. Fertilization happens when a male sex cell joins up with a female sex cell.

1 First a tube grows out of the pollen grain. It grows towards the female sex cell. A male sex cell moves down the tube.

2 The tube enters the female sex cell. The tip of the tube bursts open. The male sex cell joins up with the female sex cell. The ovule then becomes a **seed**. The ovary becomes a **fruit** with the seed inside it. The petals die and drop off.

Questions

1 What are self-pollination and cross-pollination?
2 **a)** Describe the differences between insect-pollinated, and wind-pollinated flowers.

b) Give the reasons for these differences.
3 What happens after a pollen grain lands on a stigma?

More about fruits and seeds

In biology a **fruit** is any part of a plant that contains **seeds**.

Apples, oranges, lemons and tomatoes are all fruits. Think of the seeds inside them.

Pea pods are also fruits. The peas inside them are seeds.

Nuts are fruits too. The part we eat is the seed.

How fruits and seeds get scattered

Most plants produce hundreds of seeds at a time. If they all fell close to the parent plant they would be too crowded. The new plants would have to compete with each other for water, minerals, and light.

Instead, fruits and seeds get scattered by the wind, or animals, or by the plant itself. This is called **dispersal** of fruits and seeds.

Dispersal by wind

These fruits and seeds are dispersed by the wind.

Dandelion and thistle seeds have a downy 'parachute' which floats in the wind.

Sycamore, ash, and lime seeds have wings which carry them long distances in the wind.

Poppy heads sway in the wind scattering seeds through holes in their sides.

Dispersal by animals

These fruits and seeds are dispersed by animals.

Blackberry, sloe, and hawthorn berries are eaten whole by animals. The seeds pass unharmed through their bodies.

Burdock has hooks which catch on animals' fur or on our clothes. The seeds can be carried long distances before falling off.

Acorns and beech nuts are carried away by birds and squirrels. Some are dropped before they are eaten.

Dispersal by plants

Some plants throw away their seeds.

Lupin seed pods suddenly burst open when dry. Their sides coil up, scattering the seeds.

Geranium fruits also burst open when dry. Their sides spring upwards, scattering the seeds.

Some seeds are collected and stored and sold by man. They get dispersed by gardeners and farmers.

Questions

1 In biology, what is a fruit?
2 Why do seeds need to be dispersed?
3 **a)** Name two plants that use wind dispersal.
   b) How are their fruits and seeds suited to this?
4 How do some plants disperse their own seeds?

5 Describe two ways in which animals can disperse fruits and seeds. Give an example of each.
6 Describe how you may have helped disperse seeds without knowing it.

3·8 How seeds grow into plants

A seed looks dead. But inside it there is a tiny plant called an **embryo**, and a store of food. If the seed is given water, air, and warmth it 'comes to life', and the embryo begins to grow. This is called **germination**.

The embryo in a seed has three parts. It has a root or **radicle,** a shoot or **plumule,** and one or more seed leaves called **cotyledons.** The embryo needs its stored food for growth, until it has enough leaves to make food by photosynthesis.

Bean seeds

Bean seeds have two seed leaves, so they are called **dicotyledons** (di means two). The seed leaves of beans are swollen, because they contain the stored food.

Not all seeds get a chance to grow into plants. Some are eaten first – like these baked beans.

Broad beans. The one on the left has had its seed coat removed.

Broad bean cut in half to show cotyledons and embryo.

Germination of a French bean seed

When a French bean germinates, the cotyledons come above the ground. This is called **epigeal germination**. These pictures show a French bean germinating. The brown object in two of the pictures is the seed coat which has split off the seed.

The cotyledons push their way out of the soil.

They provide the food the plant needs, until its leaves grow.

The leaves are growing, so the cotyledons will soon drop off.

Maize and other cereal grains

Maize, wheat, rice, barley, and other cereal grains have only one cotyledon. So they are called **monocotyledons** (mono means one). Their food is not stored in the cotyledon, but in a mass of cells called **endosperm** in a space above the cotyledon. When grains are milled, the endosperm spills out. We call it flour.

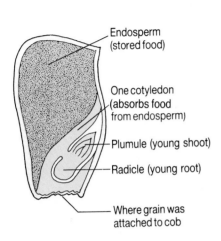

Endosperm (stored food)

One cotyledon (absorbs food from endosperm)

Plumule (young shoot)

Radicle (young root)

Where grain was attached to cob

A maize grain cut in half. Compare it with the drawing.

Tortilla

Tostada

Taco

Enchillada

We make a lot of our food by grinding up the seeds of maize, wheat and other cereals, to get their food stores. Above are some Mexican foods made from maize flour.

Germination of maize grains

When a maize grain germinates, the cotyledon stays below the ground. This is called **hypogeal germination**. Other grains, and broad beans, also germinate in this way.

A maize grain germinating. Note the root growing downwards. Its tip is protected by a root cap.

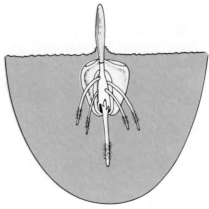

The young shoot pushes through the soil. The endosperm provides the food it needs.

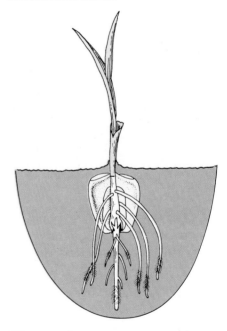

The new leaves can now make their own food. The cotyledon is still below ground.

Questions

1. What three things does a seed need to grow?
2. What is inside a seed?
3. What is:
   a) a radicle? **b)** a plumule? **c)** a cotyledon?
4. Why do seeds need a store of food?
5. Is maize grain a dicotyledon? Explain.
6. What is the main difference between epigeal germination and hypogeal germination?

3·9 Plant senses

Plants have no eyes or ears or noses. But they can still sense things. They can sense light, and the pull of gravity, and water. They respond to these things by growing slowly in certain directions. These responses are called **tropisms**.

Phototropism: response to light

Plants need light to make food. So they respond to light by growing towards it. They also turn their leaves to face the light. This makes sure leaves get as much light as possible.

These cress plants were grown with light coming from above.

These were grown with light coming from the right.

Geotropism: response to gravity

No matter how you plant a seed in the earth, it can sense which way is down, and which is up. It can sense this from the pull of gravity.

Roots grow down in response to gravity. This makes sure they find soil and water. Shoots always grow up. This makes sure they reach light.

Roots responding to gravity. Which seed was planted upside down?

Hydrotropism: response to water

Roots always grow towards water, even if this means ignoring the pull of gravity. If they have to they will grow sideways, or even upwards, to reach water.

Water

Clay plant pot   Rubber bung   Moist soil

Root grows towards water

Dry soil

Auxin

A plant's responses to light and gravity are controlled by a chemical called **auxin**. Auxin is made by cells at the tips of stems and roots. It speeds up growth in stems. It slows down growth in roots.

Phototropism and auxin

When light comes from above, auxin spreads evenly down the stem. The stem grows straight up.

When light comes from one side, auxin spreads down the *shaded* side of the stem.

Auxin makes stem cells *grow faster*. This causes the stem to bend towards the light.

Geotropism and auxin

If a plant is laid on its side auxin gathers in the lower half of the stem and root.

Auxin here *slows down* the growth of root cells. The root curves downwards.

Auxin here *speeds up* the growth of stem cells. The stem curves upwards.

Questions

1 Copy and complete:
   a) A plant's response to light is called
   _____ .

   b) A plant's response to gravity is called
   _____ .

   c) A plant's response to water is called
   _____ .

2 What does a shoot do in response to light, and in response to gravity? How are these responses useful to the plant?

3 Name two responses controlled by auxin.

4 In which parts of a plant is auxin made?

5 How does auxin affect root and shoot cells?

3·10 Asexual reproduction

Sexual reproduction needs *two* parents. They produce the male and female sex cells described in unit 3.5.

Many flowering plants can reproduce in another way, which needs only *one* parent. A plant grows parts which break off, and become new plants. This is called **asexual reproduction** or **vegetative reproduction**. Strawberry, iris, potato and gladiolius plants can reproduce this way. The photos below show how.

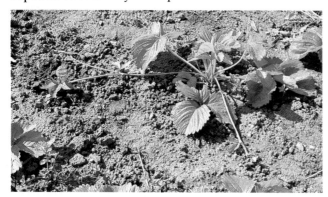

Strawberry runners. These are side shoots which grow over the soil. They have buds which grow into new plants. Then the runners die away.

Potato tubers. A potato is really an underground stem of a potato plant, swollen with stored food. The 'eyes' on the potato sprout into new plants.

Iris rhizomes. These are stems that grow sideways through the soil. They are swollen with stored food. In the spring they produce new plants.

Gladiolus corms. A corm is a short stem, swollen with stored food. The corms in the photo will separate from each other and form new plants.

Questions

1 What is the difference between sexual reproduction and asexual reproduction?

2 How do strawberry and potato plants reproduce asexually?

3 What use do plants make of food stored in tubers, corms, and rhizomes?

4 Match these words with the descriptions below: rhizome, tuber, corm, runner
   a) underground horizontal stem,
   b) short stem full of stored food,
   c) its eyes can produce new plants,
   d) grows horizontally above the ground.

3·11 Artificial propagation

You can grow many plants from one plant, by using man-made methods. This is called **artificial propagation**.

Cuttings

A cutting is part of a shoot, root, or leaf cut from a plant. The cutting grows all its missing parts to become a complete plant. Cuttings allow you to produce many new plants from one plant without waiting for flowers and seeds. The new plants are *exact* copies of the parent plant.

A cutting from a plant. See how new roots have grown.

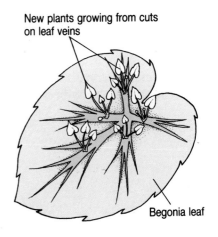

New plants growing from cuts on leaf veins

Begonia leaf

You can grow a begonia plant from a begonia leaf, by making cuts into the leaf veins and putting the leaf in water.

Grafting

You can join part of one plant onto another plant of the same sort. This is called **grafting**. To make a graft, you cut a piece off one plant and join it to a cut on another plant. The cuts soon heal, and the two parts become one plant.

Grafting is used to breed flowering bushes and fruit trees. This is useful because these plants can be very difficult to grow from seeds or cuttings.

A   B

Raffia binding

Grafting was used to grow this apple tree.

Questions

1 Why is it useful to be able to grow plants from cuttings and graftings?

2 What is the difference between a cutting and a graft?

Photosynthesis and mineral nutrition

Photosynthesis

Billions of living things all over the world are breathing in oxygen day and night to release energy from food during respiration.

Why isn't all the oxygen used up? Where do new supplies come from?

The answer is in Unit 3.1: oxygen comes from plants: they produce it as a by-product of photosynthesis.

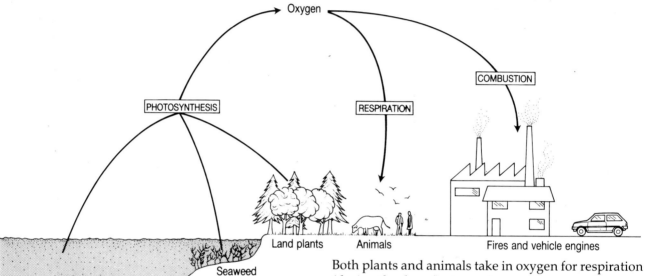

Land plants, especially trees, produce up to 80 per cent of the world's oxygen supplies. The remainder comes from marine algae (seaweeds) and phytoplankton, the countless microscopic plant-like creatures which live in the sunlit upper layers of the sea.

Both plants and animals take in oxygen for respiration (during the day plants produce more oxygen than they use for respiration). Oxygen is also used up by combustion.

1   How does oxygen get back to the plants to be recycled? Study the diagram below. It should give you one answer, another is contained in the text above.

*2   Tropical rain forests cover an area **eight** times the size of the British Isles, but are being cut down so fast that there will be little left in a few decades. Give one reason, **connected with this unit**, why their destruction could endanger all living things. What other reasons, unconnected with this unit, are there for preserving these forests?*

The oxygen cycle

Oxygen released by plants returns in two ways.
1.   Some returns as they take it in for respiration.
2.   The remaining oxygen returns in water used for photosynthesis. The diagram opposite shows that respiration produces water and some of this will find its way into plants.

It is estimated that plants recycle all the oxygen in the atmosphere once every 2000 years.

Plant mineral nutrition

Plants need more than carbon dioxide and water to thrive. Experiments have shown that they need twelve minerals as well.

Design controlled experiments using the apparatus opposite:
1   to show that plants need all twelve minerals for healthy growth (you do not have to name the minerals),
2   to show how a lack of each mineral affects plants. Why must air be bubbled through the apparatus each day?

A plant's mineral needs are discovered by growing seedlings, or cuttings, in solutions, each of which lacks just one of the essential minerals. This method shows up defects called **mineral deficiency symptoms**, some of which are illustrated below.

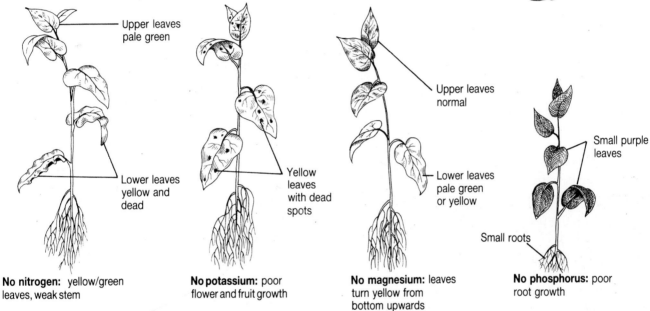

No nitrogen: yellow/green leaves, weak stem

No potassium: poor flower and fruit growth

No magnesium: leaves turn yellow from bottom upwards

No phosphorus: poor root growth

Design a table which summarizes the deficiencies illustrated above.

In what way can knowledge of mineral deficiency symptoms help farmers and gardeners?

Major elements are the minerals plants need in quite large amounts (several hundred parts per million) for healthy growth. They are nitrogen, phosphorus, sulphur, potassium, calcium and magnesium. Nitrogen is known as the leaf maker, phosphorus the root maker and potassium the flower and fruit maker. **Trace elements** are needed in very small amounts (as low as one part per million). Examples are manganese, copper, iron, boron and molybdenum.

Plants take in minerals until their sap contains higher concentrations than surrounding soil water. This shows that minerals do not simply diffuse into roots. Their absorption is a complex process which requires energy. If oxygen is bubbled through a liquid in which plants are growing mineral absorption increases, but it slows down when the oxygen is turned off, and almost stops when chemicals are added which slow down the rate of respiration.

From the information given above and in the text opposite decide which minerals should be added regularly to soil used for growing these plants:
1   tomatoes,
2   roses,
3   lettuce,
4   grass,
5   fruit bushes
Give a reason for each answer.

1 *Understanding/making predictions*

The diagram opposite shows an experiment to investigate how plants and animals interact. All the flasks were placed in bright light and kept at the same temperature.

a) Which flask would contain the most oxygen after one hour?

b) Explain your answer to (a).

c) Which flask would contain the most carbon dioxide after an hour?

d) Explain your answer to (c).

e) In which flask would the fish survive the longest?

f) Explain your answer to (e).

g) What are the controls in this experiment, and why are they necessary?

h) How does this experiment illustrate the oxygen cycle?

2 *Interpret data*

The diagram opposite shows apparatus designed to demonstrate a life process in plants. After the model was set up cotton wool in the tube gradually became red. The model was placed in different places and its weight loss recorded (see table opposite).

a) Name the parts of a plant represented by:
the plastic sheet;
pores in the plastic sheet;
the blotting paper;
the plastic tube.

b) What life processes are demonstrated when:
the cotton wool changes colour;
the apparatus loses weight.

c) Explain the experimental results.

3 *Understanding/making predictions*

The apparatus opposite is designed to investigate support in woody and non-woody (herbaceous) stems. Straight stems were placed in different liquids and a 5g weight suspended from each.

a) After three hours what would be the appearance of stems in liquid A and liquid B?

b) Explain your predictions using the words turgid, flaccid and osmosis.

c) What could this experiment tell you about how woody and non-woody stems are supported?

Experiment	Location	Weight loss
A	indoors	1.0g
B	out of doors	1.8g
C	inside plastic bag	0.1g

4 *Recall knowledge*

The diagram opposite shows the inside of a leaf.

   a) Name the parts labelled A to G.

   b) For each description below, write down the matching name and label:

cells which make food by photosynthesis;

layer of wax which makes a leaf waterproof;

hole which lets gases in and out of leaf;

contains tubes carrying sugar and water;

have chlorophyll inside them.

5 *Interpret data*

A pond contains many water plants. The graphs opposite show how the amounts of oxygen and carbon dioxide in the pond change.

   a) When does the amount of oxygen start to increase?

   b) When does the amount of oxygen stop increasing?

   c) Why does the amount of oxygen increase and decrease at these times?

   d) What happens to the amount of carbon dioxide in the pond, while the oxygen is increasing?

   e) Why does the amount of carbon dioxide change in this way?

6 *Recall knowledge*

The diagrams opposite show a stem and root.

   a) Name the parts labelled A to H.

   b) For each description below, write down the matching name and label:

      tubes which transport water from the roots;

      tubes which transport sugar from the leaves;

      cells which grow into xylem and phloem;

      protects growing cells at the root tip;

      absorbs water and minerals from the soil;

      cells which produce auxin.

7 *Interpret data*

The experiment opposite used oat seedlings that were prepared in different ways. They are growing in a box with a hole cut at one end.

   a) Which seedlings have grown towards the light?

   b) Some seedlings have not grown towards the light. Explain why.

   c) Explain how these results show that it is the tip of an oat seedling which allows it to bend towards the light.

4·1 Skeletons

Some animals, like the jellyfish in this photograph, can live without a skeleton. They are supported by the water in which they float. But without your skeleton you would collapse in a heap. Like most creatures, especially land animals, you need a skeleton to support your body and give it shape.

Jellyfish don't need skeletons since the water supports them. On land they just flop.

Animals with liquid skeletons

Earthworms, caterpillars, and slugs are given shape and support by **liquid** inside them.

This liquid is mainly water. It fills the animal's cells and the spaces inside its body. Muscles squeeze against the liquid. This keeps it at a high pressure so the body stays firm.

The worm's muscles squeeze the liquid inside its body

This liquid supports the worm's body

This will turn into a moth and get a hard external skeleton.

Animals with hard external skeletons

Insects, crabs, spiders, and other arthropods have a hard, tough skin over their bodies. This skin is like a suit of armour. It forms flat plates and hollow tubes which support and protect the body. This hard skin is called an **exoskeleton**.

Flat plates cover the body.

Hollow tubes form the limbs.

Joints allow the limbs to move.

What an exoskeleton does

1 It **supports** the body and gives it shape.

2 It **protects** the soft insides from damage, dirt, and germs.

3 It is **waterproof** and stops the body drying up.

4 Its **colour** may help the animal to hide, or attract a mate.

5 Muscles are attached to it to move the joints.

A crab grows by shedding its exoskeleton. The skin beneath then hardens to form a new one.

A male stag beetle has antlers as part of its exoskeleton. It uses them to fight for females.

Animals with hard internal skeletons

You are supported by a hard skeleton inside your body, called an **endoskeleton**. It is made of bone. Fish, amphibia, reptiles, birds, and mammals all have endoskeletons.

The **skull** protects the brain, eyes, and inner ears.

Ribs protect the heart, lungs, and main blood vessels.

Muscles are attached to bones. They can pull on the bones and make them move.

The **backbone** is the body's main support. It also protects the nerve cord — the body's main nerve.

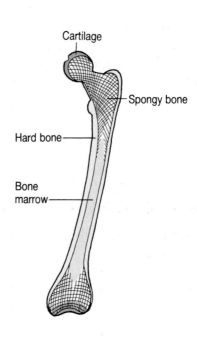

This is a leg bone cut in half. Bones are alive. They contain cells called **bone marrow** which make blood.

Questions

1 lobster mackerel housefly sparrow cat
Which of these have exoskeletons and which have endoskeletons?

2 What part of your skeleton protects:
a) your heart? b) your eyes? c) your nerve cord?

3 Does this describe an endoskeleton or an exoskeleton?
a) It stops the body drying up.
b) It makes blood cells.
c) It keeps dirt and germs out of the body.
d) It is waterproof.

4·2 More about the human skeleton

There are about 200 bones in your skeleton. This is a simple diagram showing the main ones.

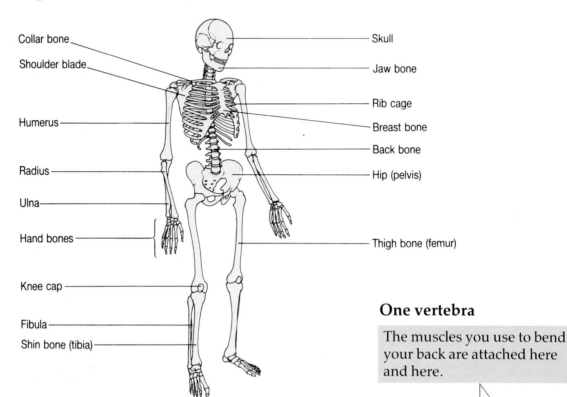

Collar bone

Shoulder blade

Humerus

Radius

Ulna

Hand bones

Knee cap

Fibula

Shin bone (tibia)

Skull

Jaw bone

Rib cage

Breast bone

Back bone

Hip (pelvis)

Thigh bone (femur)

The backbone

The backbone is called the **vertebral column**. It is made up of 33 small bones called **vertebrae**. These are joined in such a way that the backbone can bend and twist. This drawing shows part of a vertebral column seen from one side.

Intervertebral discs are pads of cartilage between the vertebrae. They stop vertebrae knocking against each other when you run or jump.

One vertebra

The muscles you use to bend your back are attached here and here.

This vertebra rubs against the next one here and here.

The vertebra has a hollow centre. The nerve cord goes through it.

Joints

Joints occur wherever two or more bones touch. There are three kinds of joint:

1   fixed joints where the bones cannot move. There are fixed joints between the bones that make up the roof of your skull.

2   slightly moveable joints where the bones can move a little. There are slightly moveable joints between your vertebrae.

3   freely moveable joints where the bones can move easily. There are freely moveable joints at your knees and elbows.

A human skull seen from above. The lines are the fixed joints.

Parts of a joint

The bones at a joint are held together by strong fibres called **ligaments**.

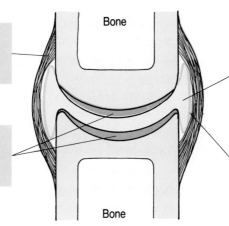

An oily liquid called **synovial fluid** helps the joint move smoothly.

Where the bones rub together they are covered by a slippery layer of **cartilage**.

The **synovial membrane** around the joint stops the synovial fluid from draining away.

Two types of freely moveable joint

Hinge joints can bend in only one direction, like the hinge of a door. Your elbow is a hinge joint.

Ball-and-socket joints can bend in all directions. An example is the joint at your hip.

The hip joint from a human skeleton. Why is it called a ball and socket joint?

Questions

1   Write down the everyday names for these bones:
   a) pelvis **b)** vertebral column **c)** femur
   d) tibia

2   Where are your intervertebral discs, and what are they for?

3   What are ligaments for?

4   Name a hinge joint and a ball-and-socket joint on your body which are not mentioned here.

5   What is synovial fluid for?

6   What is cartilage for?

Muscles and movement

Muscles work by getting shorter, or **contracting**. When a muscle contracts it pulls what it is joined to, or squeezes something. There are three kinds of muscle in your body: **voluntary, involuntary** and **cardiac**.

Voluntary muscles

Voluntary muscles are muscles that you can control as you wish (voluntary means by free will).

The muscles attached to your bones are voluntary. When you decide to move they pull on your bones, which makes your joints bend. These muscles work quickly and powerfully, but they soon get tired.

Stripes

Nucleus

Voluntary muscles are made of fibres which are long and striped.

Involuntary muscles

Involuntary muscles are those you cannot control. They keep working on their own.

There are involuntary muscles in the walls of your gut. Their job is to push food along the gut. Involuntary muscles are also found in the walls of blood vessels, and the bladder. Involuntary muscles work slowly and do not get tired.

Involuntary muscle fibres

Involuntary muscles are made of short unstriped fibres.

Cardiac muscle

Your heart is made of cardiac muscle. This is a special kind of involuntary muscle.

Cardiac muscle works, without getting tired, all through your life, pumping blood around your body.

Branching muscle fibres

Cardiac muscle is made of branched fibres.

More about voluntary muscles

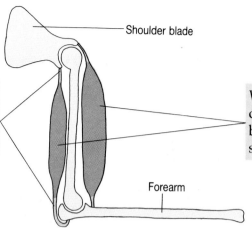

Muscles are attached to bones by strong fibres called **tendons**. A muscle has at least one tendon at each end.

Shoulder blade

When one of these muscles contracts it pulls against the bones of the arm. This bends or straightens the elbow joint.

Forearm

Voluntary muscles work in pairs

The muscles at a joint work in pairs. One muscle makes the joint bend, the other makes it straighten.

This muscle has contracted to bend or **flex** the elbow joint. Muscles which bend joints are called **flexor muscles**.

This muscle has contracted to straighten or **extend** the elbow joint. Muscles which straighten joints are called **extensor muscles**.

Questions

1 What kind of muscle:
  a) moves your arm when you turn this page?
  b) moves food from your mouth to your stomach?
  c) moves your legs when you run?
  d) moves blood around your body?

2 Why are at least two muscles needed at a joint?

3 What is the name for:
  a) muscles which straighten joints?
  b) muscles which bend joints?

4 Describe one way that heart muscle is:
  a) similar to stomach muscle.
  b) different from stomach muscle.

5 What is the difference between a ligament and a tendon?

4·4 Respiration

You use energy to walk, and think, and digest your food. In fact, you use energy for everything that goes on in your body. You get energy from food, during **respiration**.

Respiration goes on in the cells of every living thing.

Aerobic respiration

Respiration uses glucose from digested food. It usually uses oxygen too. Respiration which uses oxygen is called **aerobic respiration.** This is what happens:

Even relaxing needs energy . . . and that means respiration. It goes on in all your cells even when you are quite still or asleep.

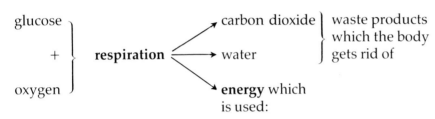

1 to work the muscles and other organs
2 to make the chemicals the body needs
3 to make new cells for growth, and to replace dead cells.

You can write aerobic respiration as:

glucose + oxygen → carbon dioxide + water + **energy**

Anaerobic respiration

Respiration can also take place without oxygen. It is then called **anaerobic respiration**. It produces less energy than aerobic respiration.

Microscopic organisms like yeast get energy by a type of anaerobic respiration called **fermentation**. It produces alcohol:

glucose → carbon dioxide + alcohol + **energy**

Alcoholic drinks are made using yeast and the sugar in fruit juice. Cider is made from yeast and apple juice. Beer is made from yeast and the malt obtained from barley seeds.

Fermentation is also used in baking. It takes place when yeast and sugar are added to dough. It produces carbon dioxide gas which fills the dough with bubbles and makes it rise. The yeast is killed in the hot oven.

Bubbles of carbon dioxide are produced when wine ferments.

Anaerobic respiration in muscles

Muscles can respire for a short time without oxygen (**anaerobically**). This happens when you run very fast. Your muscles need more energy than they can get from aerobic respiration. They get the extra energy they need from **anaerobic respiration**. This produces **lactic acid** instead of carbon dioxide.

$$glucose \rightarrow lactic\ acid + \textbf{energy}$$

Lactic acid gathers in your muscles making them ache so much that you soon have to stop running. You get rid of the lactic acid by rapid breathing after you stop. This supplies your muscles with oxygen, which combines with lactic acid to make carbon dioxide and water.

The amount of oxygen needed to get rid of lactic acid from muscles is called the **oxygen debt**.

After an exhausting race, these rowers gasp for breath to pay back the oxygen debt.

The respiratory system in humans

You use your **respiratory system** to breathe in oxygen for respiration, and to breathe out carbon dioxide produced by respiration.

The voice box or **larynx**. It makes sounds used in speaking.

The wind-pipe or **trachea**. It is like the flexible hose of a vacuum cleaner or tumble drier. It is held open by rings of **cartilage**.

The **lungs** are soft and spongy.

The **ribs** protect the lungs.

The **intercostal muscles** help with breathing in and out.

The heart

Lungs are in a space in the chest called the **thoracic cavity**.

This cavity is lined with a slippery skin called the **pleural membrane**. It protects the lungs as they rub against the ribs.

The wind pipe has thousands of branches which end in tiny **air sacs**. This is where oxygen is taken in to the body, and carbon dioxide is got rid of.

The **diaphragm** is a sheet of muscle below the lungs. It helps with breathing in and out.

Questions

1 Why is respiration essential for life?
2 What is the difference between aerobic and anaerobic respiration?
3 What waste substances are produced by aerobic respiration?
4 Which kind of respiration is going on in your body now, and which when you run very fast?
5 How does your body use the energy from food?
6 Why has the wind-pipe got rings of cartilage?
7 What is the larynx for?

Your body takes in oxygen from the air for respiration. At the same time it gives out the carbon dioxide produced by respiration. This exchange of gases takes place in your lungs.

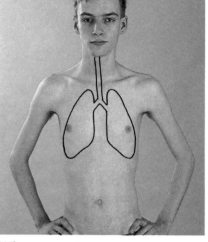

Where your lungs are . . .

The windpipe

The wind-pipe divides into two tubes called **bronchi**.

The bronchi divide thousands of times into narrower tubes called **bronchioles**.

There are **air sacs** at the ends of the bronchioles. This is where gas exchange takes place.

Bronchiole

A closer look at air sacs

This is one **air sac**. It looks like a bunch of grapes. The 'grapes' are called **alveoli**. They are smaller than grains of salt, and there are 300 million of them in your lungs.

Alveoli have thin moist walls, so that gases can pass through them easily.

One alveolus

Alveoli are covered with narrow blood vessels called **capillaries**. Oxygen passes into the capillaries from the alveoli.

Gas exchange in the alveoli

This diagram shows what happens in the alveoli.

Blood flows to the lungs from around the body. It carries carbon dioxide produced by respiration in the cells of the body.

Carbon dioxide passes *from* the blood *into* the alveoli. Then it is breathed out of the body.

Carbon dioxide   Oxygen

Blood carries oxygen away from the lungs to every cell in the body, where it is used for respiration.

Oxygen is breathed into the lungs. It dissolves in the water lining the alveoli. From there it passes *into* the blood.

When you breathe in

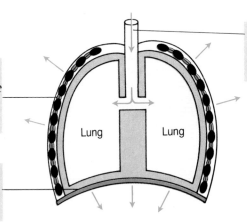

1 The **intercostal muscles** contract. These pull the rib cage upwards. So the chest increases in volume.

2 The **diaphragm** contracts. This makes it flatten out, so the chest gets even larger.

3 As the chest gets larger, air is sucked down the wind-pipe and into the lungs.

Lung   Lung

When you breathe out

1 The **intercostal muscles** relax, which lowers the rib cage. The chest decreases in volume.

2 The **diaphragm** relaxes, and bulges upwards. This decreases the volume of the chest even more.

3 Because the chest has got smaller, air is forced out of the lungs.

Lung   Lung

How air changes in your lungs

Gas	Amount of it in air you breathe in	Amount of it in air you breathe out
Oxygen	21%	16%
Carbon dioxide	0.04%	4%
Nitrogen	79%	79%
Water vapour	a little	a lot

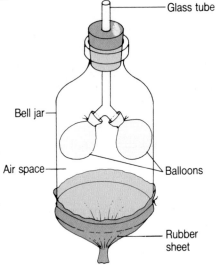

Glass tube

Bell jar

Air space

Balloons

Rubber sheet

Watch what happens in a **bell jar** when you pull the rubber sheet downwards.

Questions

1 Which gases are exchanged in your lungs?
2 Where in the lungs does gas exchange take place?
3 Explain what happens to intercostal muscles and the diaphragm as you breathe in and out.
4 Explain why you breathe out:
   a) more carbon dioxide than you breathe in
   b) as much nitrogen as you breathe in
5 Do you use *all* the oxygen your breathe in?
6 What are alveoli?

4 Respiration and breathing

External and internal respiration

The word respiration used to mean breathing; that is, the movements which draw air into and push it out of the lungs. This is now called **external respiration** because it involves the exchange of oxygen and carbon dioxide between the body and the outside world.

The modern definition of respiration is the chemical breakdown of food to produce energy for life. This is sometimes called **internal respiration** because it takes place inside every living cell.

What does external respiration supply to, and remove from living cells so that they can carry out internal respiration?

Aerobic and anaerobic respiration

In most organisms internal respiration requires oxygen and involves the *complete* breakdown of food molecules with the release of *all* available energy. This is called **aerobic respiration**. The complete breakdown of one gram molecule (180g) of glucose produces:

glucose + oxygen $\xrightarrow{\text{enzymes}}$ carbon dioxide + water + 2898kJ of energy

This shows only the raw materials and end-products of respiration. In fact it involves at least fifty different reactions each controlled by its own enzyme. These reactions take place inside structures called **mitochondria** (see photograph above).

Anaerobic respiration of one gram molecule of glucose produces:

glucose $\xrightarrow{\text{enzymes}}$ alcohol or lactic acid + 210kJ of energy

Find three major differences between aerobic and anaerobic respiration

Anaerobic respiration breaks down food without oxygen and does not release all of the available energy. Food is broken down to substances including alcohol and lactic acid.

In humans and many other organisms anaerobic and aerobic respiration occur together as a continuous process. Food is broken down in two stages (see diagram opposite). First an **anaerobic** stage breaks food down to an intermediate substance (lactic acid in humans) with the release of a little energy. Then an **aerobic** stage uses oxygen to break down the intermediate substance into carbon dioxide and water and releases all the remaining energy.

1 What happens to your breathing rate and pulse if you run as fast as you possibly can for as long as you can?
2 Why do these changes take place?
3 What eventually stops you running?

Respiration takes place inside **mitochondria**. These are tiny sausage-shaped objects in the cytoplasm of animal and plant cells which contain the enzymes needed to break down food and release energy.

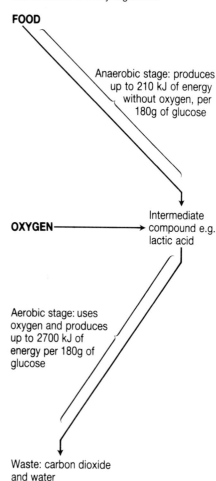

Anaerobic and aerobic respiration can be linked in many organisms

FOOD

Anaerobic stage: produces up to 210 kJ of energy without oxygen, per 180g of glucose

OXYGEN

Intermediate compound e.g. lactic acid

Aerobic stage: uses oxygen and produces up to 2700 kJ of energy per 180g of glucose

Waste: carbon dioxide and water

Aerobic and anaerobic exercises

Walking or slow running (jogging) are called **aerobic exercises** because the body can easily obtain enough oxygen for the aerobic stage of respiration to release all the energy from food and break it down completely to carbon dioxide and water. These wastes are excreted so they do not accumulate in the body. Walkers and fit joggers can continue for several hours.

Respiration is much faster during very fast running. This soon becomes **anaerobic exercise** because, no matter how fast you breathe, or how fast your heart beats, your body cannot get enough oxygen for the aerobic stage of respiration to completely break down food. The anaerobic stage of respiration continues to speed up because it does not need oxygen, but this produces lactic acid faster than it can be broken down by the aerobic stage. Within less than a minute there is so much lactic acid in the muscles that they stop working.

Why are marathon runners able to run for hours, but sprinters have to stop after a few seconds? Which of the two build up an oxygen debt (Unit 4.4)? How is this debt 'paid'?

Respiratory surfaces

Unit 4.5 explains how oxygen moves into your body through the surface of air sacs in your lungs, and carbon dioxide moves out. This is why air sacs are called your **respiratory surface**.

Why isn't your skin used as a respiratory surface?

Respiratory surfaces have these features:
1   A large surface area to give maximum contact with the air or water.
2   The surface is moist, because oxygen and carbon dioxide must dissolve in liquid before they can diffuse through.
3   They are in contact with a network of blood capillaries which carry gases to and from the surface.
4   They are extremely thin.
5   There is usually a mechanism to provide a steady flow of air or water over the surface.

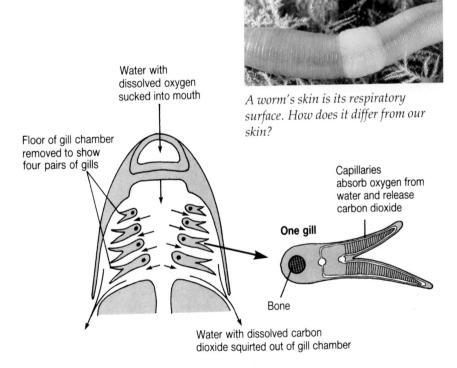

A worm's skin is its respiratory surface. How does it differ from our skin?

Water with dissolved oxygen sucked into mouth

Floor of gill chamber removed to show four pairs of gills

Capillaries absorb oxygen from water and release carbon dioxide

One gill

Bone

Water with dissolved carbon dioxide squirted out of gill chamber

The respiratory surface of a fish is its gills. Water is sucked in through the mouth, passed over the gills and out through the gill slits. How are gills different from, and similar to lungs?

85

Questions

1 *Recall knowledge/understanding*
The diagram opposite shows bones and muscles in the right leg of a runner waiting for the starting gun.

a) Give the name and letter of a ball and socket and a hinge joint.
b) What holds bones X and Z together?
c) What do flexor and extensor muscles do?
d) Which letters point to flexor muscles and which point to extensor muscles?
e) Which muscles will contract when the starting gun fires?

2 *Recall knowledge*
This diagram shows a freely moveable joint. Match each label on the diagram with one or more of the descriptions below:

a) an oily liquid;
b) slippery gristle;
c) fibres which hold the bones together;
d) synovial membrane;
e) lubricates the joint;
f) ligament.

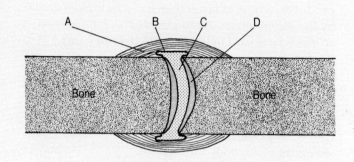

3 *Recall knowledge*
This diagram shows the parts of the human respiratory system.

Match each label on the diagram with one or more of the descriptions below:

a) holds open the wind-pipe;
b) the trachea;
c) bulges upwards when it relaxes;
d) ribs;
e) bronchus;
f) contain millions of alveoli;
g) tube connecting the mouth with the lungs;
h) lungs;
i) diaphragm;
j) lift the rib cage when they contract.

4 *Recall knowledge*
a) Name the gas your muscles produce when they are working.
b) How does your body get rid of this gas?
c) Name the gas your muscles need more of, during exercise.
d) How does this gas get to your muscles?

5 *Interpret data (extract information)*

The graphs opposite show the breathing rates of a runner before and just after a race. The distance between a peak and a trough on the graph is the volume of one breath.

a) Calculate the number of breaths per minute at rest and after running.

b) Calculate the volume of air breathed out each minute at rest and after running.

c) Explain the difference between these two volumes.

d) If unbreathed air is 20 per cent oxygen, and breathed air is 16 per cent oxygen what is the volume of oxygen taken in per minute while at rest and after running?

6 *Understanding/interpret data*

Study the apparatus in the diagram opposite. All the joints are airtight.

a) What is the purpose of this apparatus?

b) Explain the change in level of the liquid in the glass tube.

c) Why are the containers surrounded with cotton wool?

d) What is the functions of the clips?

e) What is the function of the part labelled A?

f) What control is necessary?

7 *Interpret data/understanding*

A student was given various mixtures of gas to breathe and his rate of breathing was measured. The graphs opposite show the results.

a) What is the main cause of an increase in breathing rate?

b) In view of this, why is mouth-to-mouth resuscitation normally a better method of artificial respiration than pressing down on the chest?

8 *Understanding/interpret data*

Study the apparatus in the diagram opposite. Soda lime absorbs carbon dioxide from air.

a) How far does the oil drop travel in apparatus A?

b) In view of the function of soda lime, give one reason why it moved in this way.

c) What is the apparatus measuring?

d) What is the function of apparatus B?

5

5·1 The heart

Clench your fist and look at its size. Your heart is about the same size. It is made of special muscle called **cardiac muscle**. Its job is to pump blood around your body. It pumps about 40 million times a year and weighs about as much as a grapefruit.

The outside of a heart looks like this.

This tube is a **vein**. It brings blood to the heart from all parts of the body *except* the lungs.

The heart has four compartments called **chambers**. These two upper chambers are called **atria**. (Each one is called an **atrium**.)

These two lower chambers are called **ventricles**.

These two tubes are called **arteries**. They carry blood away from the heart to all parts of the body.

The heart has its own blood supply, carried by the **coronary** artery and vein. These tubes carry food and oxygen to the heart, and carry wastes away.

Inside the heart

The atria and ventricles are hollow, so they can fill up with blood. This is a diagram of what the heart would look like sliced open.

This **artery** carries blood to the lungs.

This **valve** stops blood flowing back into the heart.

This **vein** carries blood into the heart from the body.

The **right atrium** has thin walls.

This **valve** allows blood to flow from the right atrium to the right ventricle only.

These **valve tendons** are strings which hold valve flaps in place.

The **right ventricle** has thick walls. It pumps blood to the lungs.

This **artery** carries blood away from the heart to the body.

This **vein** carries blood into the heart from the lungs.

The **left atrium** has thin walls.

This **valve** allows blood to flow from the left atrium to the left ventricle only.

The **left ventricle** has very thick walls. It pumps blood to all parts of the body, except the lungs.

How the heart pumps blood

The heart pumps blood by tightening, or **contracting.** That makes it smaller, so blood gets squeezed out into the arteries. Then it **relaxes** again, and fills up with blood from the veins.

1 When the heart is relaxed, both sides fill up with blood from the veins.

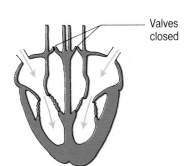

2 Then the **atria** contract. The veins also contract where they join the atria. So blood is forced into the ventricles through the valves.

This photograph shows the valve in an artery near the heart. The valve is open, so blood can flow through.

3 A fraction of a second later, the **ventricles** contract. The valves between the atria and ventricles close. So the blood is squeezed into the arteries.

4 The heart relaxes again, and fills up with blood.

One complete contraction and relaxation is called a **heartbeat**. It takes less than a second. Each beat pumps out a cupful of blood. The heart usually beats around 70 times a minute when you're resting.

This shows the same valve closed to stop blood flowing backwards into the heart.

Questions

1 What is the heart made of?

2 What are the upper parts of the heart called?

3 Which ventricle has the thickest walls?

4 What stops blood flowing backwards through the heart?

5 What are valve tendons for?

6 What are the coronary arteries and veins for?

7 The heart can **contract.** What does this mean?

8 What happens when the atria contract?

9 What happens when the ventricles contract?

10 What is a heartbeat?

11 How fast does the heart usually beat?

5·2 What makes blood flow

When the powerful muscles of your heart contract they force blood out into tubes called **arteries**. The arteries branch into tiny little tubes called **capillaries**. The capillaries join together to form **veins**. The veins carry blood back to the heart.

This is an **artery**. There are elastic fibres in its walls. The blood pumps into the artery very fast, at high pressure, so the elastic fibres stretch. Then they contract, and that squeezes the blood towards the capillaries.

This is a **capillary**. Its walls are so thin that liquid from the blood can pass through them. This liquid takes food and oxygen to the cells of the body. It also takes away carbon dioxide and other wastes.

This is a **vein**. Veins are wider than arteries and have thinner walls. The blood flows through them more slowly. They have valves to stop it flowing backwards.

An artery
Non-elastic fibres
Elastic fibres and muscle

A capillary
Wall one cell thick

A vein
Non-elastic fibres
Elastic fibres and muscle

Vein valves

There are many large veins inside muscles of the legs and arms. When these muscles contract they squeeze the veins. This squirts blood towards the heart. The valves stop it flowing in the opposite direction.

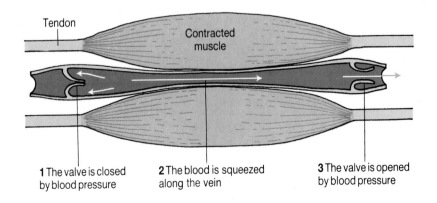

Tendon

Contracted muscle

1 The valve is closed by blood pressure
2 The blood is squeezed along the vein
3 The valve is opened by blood pressure

The circulatory system

The tubes that carry blood are called **blood vessels**. The heart and blood vessels together make up the **circulatory system**. This system has two parts:

1 The right side of the heart pumps blood to the lungs and back again. In the lungs it loses carbon dioxide and picks up oxygen.

2 The left side of the heart pumps blood to the rest of the body and back. On its way around the body the blood loses oxygen to the body cells and picks up carbon dioxide.

When the heart pumps blood into the arteries at high pressure, it causes a pulse. Use your thumb, as shown here, to find the pulse at your wrist.

This photograph shows the network of capillaries and arteries in a chick embryo. There are enough capillaries in your body to stretch one-and-a-half times round the world!

Questions

1 What happens in the arteries?

2 What happens in the capillaries?

3 How are arteries different from veins?

4 **a)** Blood is at its highest pressure just where it leaves the heart. Why do you think this is?

b) The blood in an artery flows faster and at higher pressure than the blood in a vein. Can you explain why?

5 In the diagram above find:
a) a vein with blood full of oxygen
b) an artery containing blood full of oxygen
c) a vein with blood full of digested food.

91

5·3 Heart disease

To keep pumping, your heart needs food and oxygen. It gets them from its own blood supply, carried in the **coronary arteries**. If these arteries get blocked the result is **heart disease**.

How arteries get blocked

A fatty substance called **cholesterol** can stick to the walls of an artery. The arteries become narrower. So blood gets slowed down.

Cholesterol can make artery walls rough. This causes blood to clot, as it flows past. A blood clot can block an artery completely. The blockage is called a **thrombosis**. The blood flow is stopped.

Bits of cholesterol can break off into the blood stream, and block narrow blood vessels.

A thrombosis in blood vessels in the brain is called a **stroke**. Brain cells die. A person suffering from a stroke may get paralysed or even die.

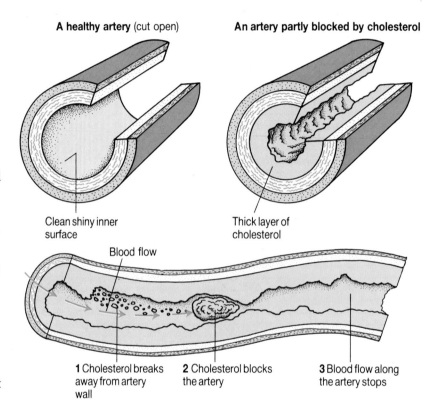

A healthy artery (cut open)

An artery partly blocked by cholesterol

Clean shiny inner surface

Thick layer of cholesterol

Blood flow

1 Cholesterol breaks away from artery wall

2 Cholesterol blocks the artery

3 Blood flow along the artery stops

Blocked coronary arteries

If a coronary artery gets partly blocked, the heart muscle gets too little food and oxygen. The result is severe chest pains, called **angina**.

A thrombosis in the coronary artery is called a **heart attack**. The heart stops beating. But with the right treatment, the heart can be forced to start beating again.

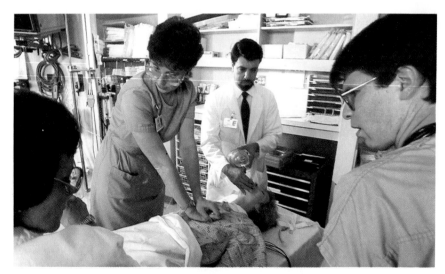

Emergency treatment for a heart attack. The victim's heart is massaged to start it beating again. The green cylinder contains oxygen.

Things that can lead to heart disease

Heart disease is a big problem. In Britain it kills about 400 people a day. Most doctors agree that your chances of suffering from it are greatest:

1   if you eat lots of cream, butter, eggs, fat, and fried foods. These can lead to a high level of cholesterol in the blood
2   if you smoke cigarettes
3   if you are overweight
4   if you take little or no regular exercise
5   if your way of life involves stress (worry, anger, fear and so on).

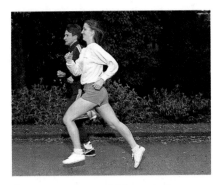

One way to avoid heart disease is to take regular exercise.

How you can avoid heart disease

1   Cut down on fried food. You can grill, boil, or steam, rather than fry. If you do fry food use corn, soya, or sunflower oils.

2   Eat less red meat. When you do eat it cut off any fat you can see.

3   Eat less dairy foods (eggs, butter, milk, and cream).

4   Eat more poultry and fish, because these are less fatty.

5   Eat more fresh fruit and vegetables.

6   Do not smoke.

7   Take exercise regularly.

8   Take time to relax before you go to bed.

If you follow these guidelines you will be less likely to suffer from heart disease. Your general health will be better too.

Questions

1   Name the fatty substance that can block arteries.
2   What is a thrombosis? What causes it?
3   What is a stroke?
4   What causes the disease called angina?
5   Explain what causes a heart attack.

6   a) Why is the man in the drawing above likely to develop heart disease?
    b) Name two things, not shown in this drawing, which can also cause heart disease.
7   How can you avoid heart disease?

5·4 What blood is

You have nearly half a bucket of blood (5.5 litres) in your body! Blood is a liquid called plasma, with red cells, white cells, and platelets floating in it. Let's look at each of these things in turn.

When blood is left standing for a time, the solid particles start settling to the bottom of the plasma.

Plasma

Plasma is a yellow liquid. It is mainly water, with digested food, hormones, and waste substances dissolved in it.

Red cells

Red blood cell (magnified 500 times)

Red cell cut in half

Haemoglobin

Red cells are wheel-shaped. They have no nucleus. They are red in colour because of the **haemoglobin** inside them.

There are about five million red cells in one drop of blood. This photograph shows them moving through a capillary.

How the red cells carry oxygen

Red cells are the body's oxygen carriers. They carry oxygen from the lungs to all the cells of the body.

1 The red cells pick up oxygen as blood is pumped through the lungs.

2 The oxygen and haemoglobin join to form **oxyhaemoglobin**. This is bright red.

3 As the blood passes around the body, the oxyhaemoglobin breaks down and releases oxygen to the body cells.

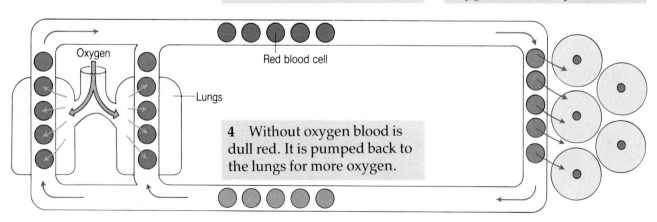

Oxygen

Red blood cell

Lungs

4 Without oxygen blood is dull red. It is pumped back to the lungs for more oxygen.

White cells

White cells are larger than red cells. They all have a **nucleus.** They can change shape. White cells protect us from disease. White cells called **phagocytes** can eat up the germs that cause disease.

Two phagocytes in a human lung. One has grown long and thin, and is about to destroy a small particle. Phagocytes keep lungs clear of dust and pollen.

1 Phagocytes can squeeze through capillary walls.

2 They move towards germs and surround them. They then digest them.

Other white cells make chemicals called **antibodies.** These chemicals destroy germs that get into the body by making them stick together, or by dissolving them. They also destroy **toxins** (poisons) that germs make. There is a different antibody for each kind of germ.

A cut healing. The tangled pink fibres were produced by the platelets. The orange bits are trapped red cells.

Platelets

Platelets are fragments of cells formed in bone marrow. Their job is to help stop bleeding from cuts.

1 Bleeding washes out dirt and germs from the cut. Then the platelets produce tiny fibres. Red cells get trapped in these fibres and the blood changes into a thick red jelly called a blood clot.

2 The clot hardens to a scab. This keeps the wound clean while new skin grows. Then the scab breaks off.

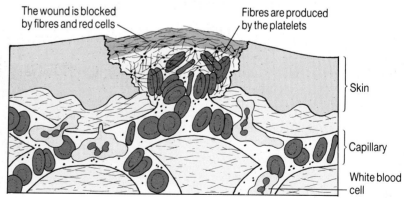

Questions

1 Name the four things that make up blood.

2 Name the liquid part of blood.

3 What do red cells do?

4 What are phagocytes?

5 What are antibodies?

6 How do platelets help blood clot?

5·5 What blood does

Blood does two jobs. It carries things round the body, and it protects us against disease.

Blood carries things

What it carries	How carried
1 Oxygen from the lungs to the rest of the body	In the red cells
2 Carbon dioxide from the body to the lungs	Mainly in plasma
3 Digested food from the gut to the rest of the body	In the plasma
4 Wastes from the liver to the kidneys	In the plasma
5 Hormones from hormone glands to where they are needed	In the plasma
6 Heat from the liver and muscles to the rest of the body so it is all at the same temperature	In all parts of the blood

Blood protects us

1   White cells called **phagocytes** eat germs.

2   Other white cells make **antibodies** to fight disease. Antibodies destroy the germs that cause disease. Antibodies also destroy toxins that germs make. There is a different antibody for each disease.

Once your white cells have made a particular kind of antibody, they can make it faster next time. Also it may stay in your blood for a while. This makes you **immune** to the disease. You will not catch it again, or else you will have only a mild attack.

You can get **vaccinated** against some diseases. Specially treated germs are injected into you, to give you a mild attack of the disease. Your body makes antibodies, so you become immune for the future.

Often, ill people need blood transfusions. The blood comes from donors. It is sent out to hospitals in plastic packs.

Questions

1   What part of the blood:
   a) carries digested food?
   b) helps protect you against disease?

2   Describe two ways in which your body can become immune to a disease.

3   What do antibodies do?

5·6 How oxygen and food reach cells

Blood carries oxygen and food around the body. But it never comes into contact with body cells. So how does food and oxygen get from the blood to the cells where they are needed?

Tissue fluid

The answer is that capillary walls are so thin that they leak. A liquid called **tissue fluid** leaks through them from the blood, into tiny spaces between the body cells.

Tissue fluid carries oxygen and food from the blood to the cells, and washes away their wastes.

Most tissue fluid then seeps back into the blood vessels. But some drains into **lymph capillaries**, carrying germs and bits of dead cells with it. It becomes **lymph**.

Where does the lymph go?

The lymph capillaries join to make larger tubes. These tubes drain into **lymph glands**.

Here the lymph is cleaned up by white cells called **lymphocytes**. These eat the germs and dead cells, and also make antibodies.

Clean lymph is returned to the blood stream through tubes which join a vein in the neck.

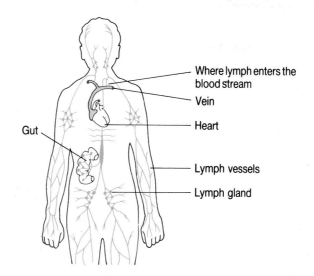

Questions

1 How does food and oxygen reach your body cells?

2 What happens to tissue fluid after it has been to the cells?

3 What happens inside lymph glands?

4 How does lymph get back into the blood stream?

5 Where in your body are the lymph glands?

5·7 Skin and temperature

Skin highly magnified. You can see the dead cells flaking off. What do you think the spike is?

What skin does

1 It **protects** your body against damage, dirt, and germs.

2 It contains millions of tiny **sense organs**, which are sensitive to touch, temperature, and pain.

3 It **excretes** water and salts from your body, as **sweat**.

4 It helps keep your body at a **steady temperature**.

The structure of skin

This is a drawing of a tiny piece of skin, greatly magnified.

The **outer layer** of your skin is a tough protective layer made of dead, flat cells. Dead cells continually flake off. But they are replaced by cells from below, which grow and flatten out as they move to the surface.

Sebaceous glands produce an oily substance called **sebum**. This makes skin and hair supple and waterproof. It also slows the growth of germs.

The **hair root** is the only living part of a hair. It is deep inside the skin in a tube – the **hair follicle**. Hair protects your head from direct sunlight and, in hairy animals, keeps the body warm.

- Hair
- Pore
- Capillaries near surface of the skin
- Blood vessel

This layer of cells is full of **fat and oil**. It helps keep the body warm.

Sweat glands produce liquid called sweat, to cool the body when it gets too hot.

Skin colour

Some skin cells make melanin, the brown pigment responsible for skin colour. Skin makes more melanin in sunshine, because melanin protects it from the sun's harmful ultraviolet rays.

Dark skin contains more melanin than pale skin does.

Skin and body temperature

The outside of your body may feel hot or cold. But inside, it always stays at about the same temperature, 37°C. Your skin helps to keep it at this temperature.

When you get too hot:

1 You sweat a lot. The sweat evaporates and cools you down.

2 The blood vessels below your skin **expand**. So a lot of blood flows near your body surface and loses heat – like a radiator.

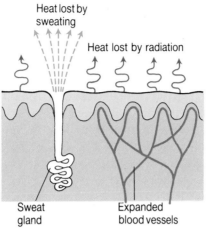

Heat lost by sweating

Heat lost by radiation

Sweat gland

Expanded blood vessels

But your skin alone won't keep you cool in hot weather...

When you get too cold:

1 You stop sweating.

2 Blood vessels below the skin **contract**. So only a little blood flows near the surface and loses heat.

3 Muscles start rapid, jerky movements we call **shivering**. This produces extra heat, which warms up the body.

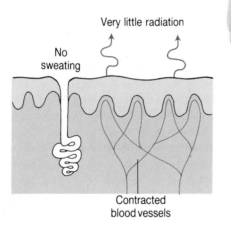

Very little radiation

No sweating

Contracted blood vessels

...or warm in cold weather. You help it out by wearing the right kind of clothes.

Body hair

Many animals have a thick coat of hair, or fur. This traps a layer of warm air around the body.

In cold weather, tiny muscles make the hairs stand up. So more air is trapped. In warm weather the hair muscles relax. So less air is trapped.

A seal pup, all dressed up for arctic life.

Questions

1 Your skin is being worn away all the time. How is it replaced?

2 How is skin protected by a suntan?

3 What changes happen in your skin when you get too hot?

4 What changes happen in your skin when you go from a warm room out into a cold winter night?

5 How does fur help artic animals to keep warm?

5·8 Excretion

Where your kidneys are...

All day long, even while you sleep, your body produces waste substances. These wastes include carbon dioxide and urea.

Your body must get rid of these things as they are poisonous. Waste removal is called **excretion**. Your lungs excrete carbon dioxide. Your kidneys excrete urea. Your kidneys are your main **excretory organs** – they are towards the back of your body just above your waist.

What kidneys do

Your kidneys remove urea, water, and other unwanted substances from your blood. Urea is a waste produced by your liver.

The **renal artery** carries 'dirty' blood to the kidneys.

The **kidneys** remove urea and other wastes from blood, and excrete it in a liquid called **urine**.

Ureters are tubes which carry urine to the bladder.

The **bladder** is a bag which stores urine until you go to the toilet.

The **renal vein** carries 'clean' blood away from the kidneys.

The **sphincter** is a ring of muscle which keeps the bladder closed until you go to the toilet.

The **urethra** is a tube which carries urine out of your body.

How kidneys clean blood

Kidneys clean blood by filtering it. They filter all your blood 300 times a day. The filtering is done by over a million tiny tubes packed into each kidney. These tubes are called **nephrons**.

Some people's kidneys are not very good at filtering blood. Kidney machines help by filtering their blood for them. The little girl in the photograph is attached to a kidney machine.

Surgeons can sometimes replace faulty kidneys with healthy ones. This operation is called a **kidney transplant**.

The parts of a kidney

This diagram shows a kidney cut in half, with one nephron magnified.

A **nephron** begins with a cup-shaped bag containing a bunch of capillaries called a **glomerulus**. 'Dirty' blood enters a glomerulus and is filtered.

Filtered liquid enters this tube-shaped part of a nephron. Here it is turned into **urine**.

The urine from many nephrons drains into a **collecting duct**.

The urine drains into the **ureter**.

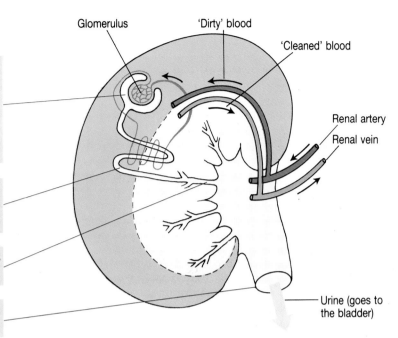

How a nephron works

The diagram below shows one nephron straightened out.

Blood is **filtered** by the glomerulus. Nearly all the blood except red cells filters through into the nephron.

The liquid in the nephron contains useful substances like glucose and vitamins as well as urea. These useful substances pass back into the blood – they are **reabsorbed**.

The liquid left in the nephron is **urine**. It contains urea and water plus other unwanted substances. It goes through the collecting ducts and ureters to the bladder.

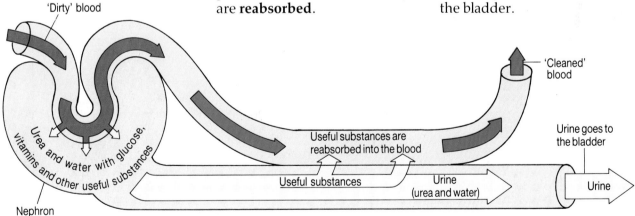

Questions

1 Why would you die if excretion stopped?
2 What do lungs and kidneys excrete?
3 What do the bladder and sphincter do?

4 Where is 'dirty' blood filtered?
5 What happens to stop useful substances being lost from the body as urine is produced?

5·A Homeostasis

Tissue fluid – your internal environment

Imagine you are an *Amoeba* in a pond. Water temperature will vary between very warm and freezing cold; some days the water will be clear and pure and on other days it could be dirty or polluted with pesticide from a nearby farm, and its oxygen content could be more than enough or so little that you nearly suffocate.

The cells of your body are in a kind of pond. They are bathed in a 'pond' of liquid called **tissue fluid** (Unit 5.6). Tissue fluid forms the **internal environment** in which the cells of your body live. Study the picture and caption opposite before reading further.

The internal environment of your body does not change all the time like pond water. Many organs work day and night making constant adjustments to keep it as near perfect an environment as possible for health, growth and efficient functioning of cells. This maintenance of a constant internal environment is called **homeostasis**.

Think about one cell somewhere in your body. Will the temperature, oxygen content and cleanliness of the surrounding tissue fluid vary like pond water around this Amoeba? If not, why not?

Homeostasis and feedback mechanisms

The boy on the pogo stick could fall sideways if he did not make constant adjustments to his balance. Messages from his eyes and balance organs travel to his brain to keep him up to date about the position of his body. His brain responds by sending messages to the muscles which control his movements. Then his sense organs 'feed back' more information to his brain so it can check that this response was correct, and so on. Identify the three parts of this feedback mechanism. What part might feedback play in homeostasis?

Homeostasis is controlled by **feedback** mechanisms, which consist of three parts. A **sense organ** detects a change somewhere in the body's internal environment and sends information about the change to a **control centre**, usually the brain. This sends messages to a **responding organ**, which makes adjustments. Feedback now occurs as the sense organ detects these adjustments and sends more information to the control centre which modifies its messages to the responding organ, whose response is detected by the sense organ, and so on.

These non-stop adjustments happen all your life, without you being aware of them.

The three parts of a typical feed-back mechanism

The organs of homeostasis

Your skin helps to keep your body within 1°C either side of 37°C (Unit 5.7). This is done by the action of sweat glands, a layer of fat under the skin, and the shivering action of muscles which generates extra heat. Hairy animals have tiny muscles attached to each hair which can contract and make them 'stand on end'. This happens in cold weather and helps prevent heat loss by trapping a layer of warm air next to the skin. Since it does not have a thick layer of hair your body can only keep at 37°C without clothes provided the air temperature does not drop below 27°C. If body temperature drops as little as 2°C below normal, movements and speech become slow and you feel very sleepy. This is called **hypothermia**.

Your liver and pancreas together control the amount of glucose in blood and tissue fluid. If the level of glucose falls below normal, glands in the pancreas produce the hormone **glucagon** which stimulates the liver to release glucose into the blood. If the glucose level rises above normal these glands release the hormone **insulin** which has the opposite effect – it stimulates the liver to remove glucose from the blood. The liver also controls the amounts of amino acids in and removes poisons from the blood and tissue fluid, and helps keep the body warm (Unit 6.7).

Your kidneys keep blood and tissue fluid 'clean' by removing urea, excess water and other wastes and excreting them (Unit 5.8). This controls the amounts of dissolved substances in blood and tissue fluid, a process called **osmoregulation**.

Your lungs control the amount of carbon dioxide and oxygen in tissue fluid (Unit 4.5).

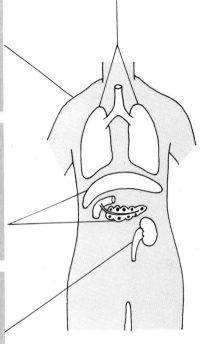

Osmoregulation

Reabsorption of useful substances by the nephrons of the kidneys (Unit 5.8) controls the amount of water and dissolved materials in blood and tissue fluid. If you drink a glass of water the water content of your blood rises. This is detected by special sense organs and your kidneys respond by reabsorbing less water from urine, so a greater amount of more dilute urine is excreted.

If you eat some sweets your blood sugar level rises. Your kidneys respond by reducing the amount of sugar they reabsorb from urine, so more is excreted from the body.

Kidney dialysis machines

In a kidney machine (page 100) blood is taken from the patient and passed into visking tubing (semi-permeable membrane). Substances with small molecules like urea and glucose diffuse out of the blood through the membrane and are washed away. 'Cleaned' blood is returned to the patient. Study the diagram opposite and text below.

In this experiment glucose, but not starch appeared in the water surrounding the visking tubing. What does this tell you about the tubing? What part of a kidney does the tubing represent? Describe one very important difference between urine produced by kidneys, and the 'urine' produced by kidney machines.

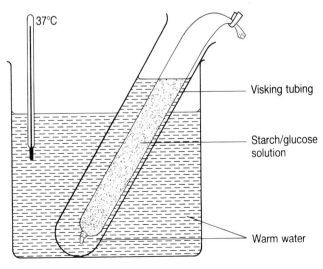

37°C

Visking tubing

Starch/glucose solution

Warm water

5·B The circulatory system

The need for a circulatory system

To remain alive you must take in food and oxygen which must be transported to every cell of your body. Cells produce carbon dioxide and other wastes which must be transported to excretory organs and removed. These substances are transported by your circulatory system (Units 5.1 to 5.6). But some organisms have no circulatory system. How can they manage without one? Carry out the task described opposite before reading further.

1 Weigh out 50 g of Plasticine, mould it into a cube and calculate its surface area and volume. Then calculate the ratio of surface area to volume.

2 Weigh out 100 g of Plasticine and do the same things.

3 What happens to these ratios as volume decreases?

Transport in microscopic organisms

As volume decreases the ratio of surface area to volume increases. In other words microscopic creatures have a relatively large surface area compared with bigger creatures.

In protozoa and many other microscopic creatures surface area is great enough to let substances diffuse in and out of the body with sufficient speed to supply all its needs without a transport system.

Study the diagram opposite. What is meant by a concentration gradient? Why does oxygen diffuse into the cell and carbon dioxide diffuse out?

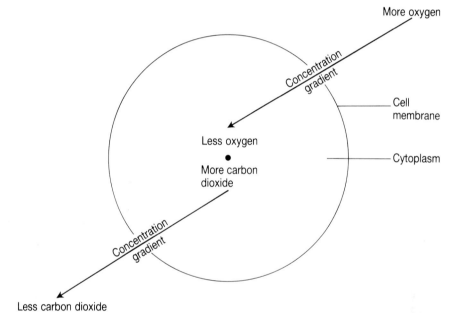

Inside an *Amoeba*, or other unicellular organism, oxygen is continually used up, so it will be less concentrated there than in surrounding pond water. Consequently oxygen will diffuse down a **concentration gradient** from the water to the centre of the cell. Carbon dioxide will diffuse in the opposite direction because it is continually produced in the cell.

Transport in large organisms

At a certain size body volume becomes so great that diffusion alone is too slow to supply its needs. Oxygen cannot diffuse from the surface to all parts, and carbon dioxide cannot diffuse out fast enough to stop it accumulating to dangerous levels.

Your body's circulatory system is so vast that not one of your many billions of cells is more than a fraction of a millimetre from a capillary blood vessel. Capillaries are so small that fifteen side by side equal the width of a hair.

Lung capillaries. This was made by injecting blood capillaries with latex rubber then using enzymes to digest away all other tissues.

Heart beat and pulse

Study the text opposite before reading further.

The main difference between heart (cardiac) muscle and muscle which moves the body is that the heart does not fatigue (get tired) despite continuous rapid contraction over many years. The heart of a non-athletic adult beats between 65 and 70 times a minute at rest, rising to 150 or more during exercise. This means it beats over 100 000 times a day and pumps about 14 000 litres of blood. Now study the graph and text opposite.

1 Open and close your hand about 70 times a minute for two or three minutes. Does your hand begin to feel tired? Could you go on doing this non-stop for years and years?

2 What does this tell you about the difference between heart muscle and muscles which move your body?

Pulse rate changes with age and fitness. Very young children have a high pulse rate because of the high metabolic rate needed to maintain growth. Fitness training slows pulse rate for two reasons. Exercise both strengthens heart muscle and makes the heart bigger, so it can pump the same amount of blood as before at a slower rate. Also body muscles become more efficient so they need less oxygen to do the same amount of work.

1 The graph shows resting pulse rates from birth to 18 years. Try to explain these changes.

2 The pulse of an unfit 45-year-old man was tested before and after a period of fitness training. Before training his resting pulse was 78 rising to 168 after exercise. These rates fell to 48 and 140 after nine months training. How could his heart and body muscles have changed to account for this result.

Control of heart beat. Your heart has a built-in speed controller called a **pacemaker**. It keeps your heart beating by sending tiny, regular electric shocks through its muscles. The rate at which shocks are sent out depends on your need for oxygen. If, after a heart attack, the pacemaker stops working, an artificial, battery operated one can be used. This is small enough to be inserted under the skin and sends shocks to the heart through wires.

Capillary beds.   The main function of the circulatory system is to deliver blood loaded with oxygen and food at high pressure to the capillaries. These form a network of tiny blood vessels called **capillary beds** which weave in and out among body cells. All the blood's functions depend on the fact that capillary walls are so thin they leak tissue fluid, which carries food and oxygen to the cells. Loss of fluid makes blood a more concentrated solution by the time it reaches the end of a capillary bed. This allows it to soak up by osmosis most of the tissue fluid returning from the cells. Lymph vessels take in the remaining tissue fluid.

Questions

1 *Recall knowledge*
This diagram shows the inside of the heart.
Match the labels on the diagram with the
descriptions below:
 a) righ atrium;
 b) blood on its way around the body;
 c) valve tendon;
 d) right ventricle;
 e) a vein carrying blood from around the
 body;
 f) left ventricle;
 g) valve which stops blood flowing back into
 the left atrium;
 h) cardiac muscle;
 i) blood on its way to the lungs;
 j) blood returning from the lungs;
 k) valve which stops blood flowing into the
 left ventricle.

2 *Recall knowledge/understanding*
Opposite is a simpler version of the diagram
from page 91, showing the heart and main blood
vessels.

Which of the blood vessels labelled 1 to 4:
 a) contains blood at the highest pressure in
 the whole body?
 b) contains blood at very low pressure?
 c) contains blood full of carbon dioxide?
 d) contains blood full of oxygen?

3 *Recall knowledge*
 a) Explain what these medical words mean:
 angina, thrombosis, heart attack.
 b) Why is it important not to eat too much
 fatty food?
 c) Name ten foods which contain lots of fat.
 d) Apart from fatty food, what else can cause
 heart disease?
 e) List all the things you should do to avoid
 heart disease.

4 *Recall knowledge*
This is a drawing of human blood cells.
 a) Name each cell.
 b) Which of the cells:
  contains haemoglobin?
  is a phagocyte?
  can pass through capillary walls?
  transports oxygen?
  eats germs?

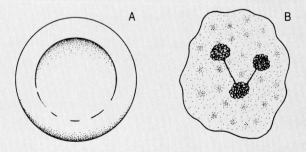

5 *Recall knowledge*

This diagram shows part of the human skin:

a) Name the parts labelled A to H.

b) Name the parts which help to control body temperature.

c) What do these parts do when we get too hot?

d) What do these parts do when we get too cold?

e) Explain how part B is replaced as fast as it wears away.

f) Why does layer H grow thicker in wild animals in autumn?

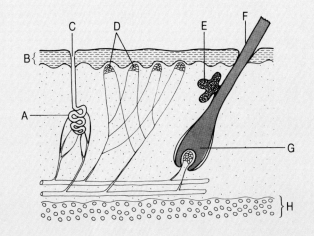

6 *Understanding/interpret data*

A student was put in the same environmental conditions and given the same food and drink for two days. She rested completely on one day and performed regular exercises on the other. The water she lost in sweat and urine was measured (see table opposite).

a) Which environmental conditions should be kept the same for the two days?

b) Why should food and drink be kept the same for the two days?

c) Explain the differences in sweat production for the two days.

d) On the exercise day what is the advantage of producing more sweat and less urine?

	Loss of water	
	Sweat	**Urine**
Rest day	100g	1900g
Exercise day	5000g	500g

7 *Understanding/interpret data*

The graph opposite shows how body temperature in humans and lizards changes with external temperature.

a) What is the body temperature of humans and lizards when the external temperature is 5°C and 30°C?

b) Which is likely to be the most active in cold weather? Explain your answer.

c) How does the human body maintain the temperatures shown on the graph?

d) What are the advantages of this ability?

e) Think of some reasons why lizards do not have this ability?

f) What could a lizard do to prevent its body over heating?

6 6·1 Food

Why we need food

For growth and repair. Your body grows by forming new cells. You also need new cells to replace dead ones. Cells are built from substances in food.

For energy. You need energy to work your muscles, and all other organs. The energy in food is measured in **calories** or in kilojoules.
(4.2 kilojoules = 1 Calorie)

To stay healthy. You need vitamins and minerals in food. This shows what happens to gums if you don't get enough vitamin C.

What's in food

Food contains a mixture of substances. The main ones are proteins, carbohydrates, fats, oils, vitamins, minerals, fibre, and water.

These eggs contain:

| 55.3 g of protein | + | 0 g of carbo-hydrate | + | 49 g of fat | + | 0.3 g of vitamins and minerals | + | 337 g of water | + | 0 g of fibre | = 2754 KJ of ENERGY |

These beans contain:

| 21.6 g of protein | + | 43.7 g of carbo-hydrate | + | 2 g of fat | + | 0.2 g of vitamins and minerals | + | 314.5 g of water | + | 31 g of fibre | = 1147 KJ of ENERGY |

What foods do for you

Carbohydrates give energy. Sugar and starch are two types of carbohydrate.

You cannot digest **dietary fibre**. But it prevents constipation and cleans your bowels.

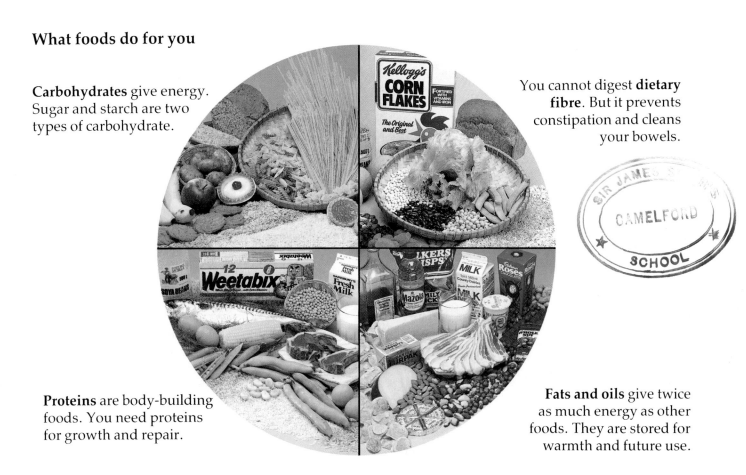

Proteins are body-building foods. You need proteins for growth and repair.

Fats and oils give twice as much energy as other foods. They are stored for warmth and future use.

The main vitamins and minerals you need

Substance	Where you find it	Why you need it	Shortage can cause
Vitamin C	Oranges, lemons, grapefruit, green vegetables, potatoes	For healthy skin and gums and to heal wounds quickly	**Scurvy.** Gums and nose bleed. The body bleeds inside
Vitamin D	Milk, butter, eggs, fish, liver (also made by skin in sunshine)	For strong bones and teeth	**Rickets.** The bones become soft and bend
Calcium	Milk, eggs	For strong bones and teeth	**Rickets.**
Iron	Liver, spinach	For making red blood cells	**Anaemia.** The person is pale and has no energy

Questions

1 Name three foods rich in:
   a) dietary fibre
   b) sugar
   c) protein
   d) starch
   e) fats and oils.

2 Name foods needed:
   a) for strong bones and teeth
   b) to avoid scurvy
   c) to avoid constipation
   d) for warmth
   e) for growth.

6·2 Eating for health

If you ate only sweets, or cream buns, or crisps you would stay alive for a time. But you would not stay healthy, because you are not eating a balanced diet.

A **balanced diet** is one which contains the right amounts of protein, carbohydrate, fat, vitamins, and minerals to satisfy all your body's needs.

How much should you eat?

The amount of food you need depends on the energy you use in a day. And that depends on:

1   your age. Teenagers use more energy than babies

2   your work. A footballer uses more energy than a snooker player

3   your sex. Males use more energy than females of the same age, even for the same work

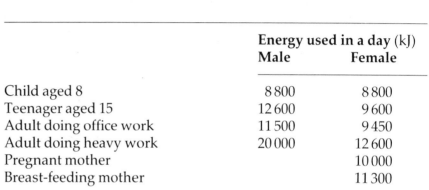

	Energy used in a day (kJ)	
	Male	Female
Child aged 8	8 800	8 800
Teenager aged 15	12 600	9 600
Adult doing office work	11 500	9 450
Adult doing heavy work	20 000	12 600
Pregnant mother		10 000
Breast-feeding mother		11 300

This table shows the amount of energy used in a day.
Energy used by the body is measured in kilojoules (kJ for short).

Getting the balance right

The food you eat each day should supply just enough energy to get you through that day.

If you eat too much, your body stores the extra as fat. So you get overweight, or **obese**. Obese people are more likely to have heart attacks than slim people.

If you eat too little, you lose weight. You feel weak and have no energy. Some people eat so little that they suffer from **anorexia**. This happens if a person starts a slimming diet and doesn't know when to stop. But we have to eat to live – so get the balance right.

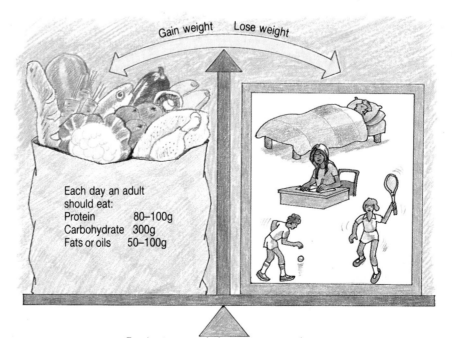

Gain weight   Lose weight

Each day an adult should eat:
Protein   80–100g
Carbohydrate 300g
Fats or oils   50–100g

Food eaten must **balance** energy used

Healthy eating

Some foods are bad for you if you eat too much of them. So it makes sense to eat healthy foods, and avoid those which can damage your health.

A little fat gives you a *lot* of energy. So it is easy to eat more than you need. Fats make you fat, and can cause heart disease.

Sugar gives you energy but nothing else. It rots your teeth and also makes you fat. Cakes, chocolate, and ice cream also contain hidden fat.

During processing in factories, food loses dietary fibre and other goodness. Salt, sugar, colouring, and other chemicals are added. These may do you harm.

These foods contain protein but not much fat. They build you up without making you fat.

These give you carbohydrate, protein and fibre. They fill you up without making you fat.

These foods contain dietary fibre, vitamins, and minerals to keep you healthy.

Questions

1   Name the five types of food which make up a balanced diet.
2   Why does a teenager need more food than a baby?
3   What happens if you eat more than you need?
4   What happens if you eat less than you need?

5   Explain why you should:
    a)   eat less cakes and ice cream
    b)   cut most of the fat from meat
    c)   eat fresh food instead of processed food
    d)   eat more fruit and vegetables.
6   Name five foods that contain fibre.

6·3 Food additives

Yum – additives!

When food is processed in factories, chemicals called **food additives** are often added.

Around 3500 additives are used by British food manufacturers. Below are the main kinds.

Colourings make food look more appetizing. Tinned peas and strawberries owe their bright colours to added chemicals. Egg yolks are given a brighter colour by chemicals put in hen food.

Flavourings put back flavours lost when food is processed in factories. They are sometimes used instead of 'real' flavours. Fruit-flavoured puddings and drinks owe their taste to chemicals and not real fruit.

Preservatives help to keep food fresh. So food can be stored in shops for some time before it goes bad. Pork pies, sausages, bacon, and dried fruits have preservatives in them.

Are additives dangerous?

There is no proof that additives cause serious illness in humans. But here are a few reasons why some people avoid eating these chemicals:

1 Additives fed to animals have caused damage to their kidneys, liver, and digestive system, and some have caused cancers.

2 Some additives destroy vitamins in food. For example, the preservative sulphur dioxide destroys vitamin B_1.

3 Some may cause asthma, itchy skin, headaches, and **hyperactivity** (uncontrollable behaviour) in young children.

If you want food free of additives, eat fresh vegetables and fresh fruit, fresh meat, real-fruit juices and yoghurt, and muesli.

Black Forest Gateau

INGREDIENTS

Sponge: Wheat flour, sugar, liquid egg, water, cocoa powder, dried skimmed milk, glucose, emulsifiers E471 E475, starch, salt, flavouring, colours E102 E122 E124 E142 155. Filling and Decoration: Cream (cream, dextrose, stabiliser E407), cherry topping (cherries, sugar, glucose, modified starch E1422, citric acid E330, flavouring, colours E123 E142 E422, thickener E412, preservative E211), chocolate flavoured coating (sugar, vegetable fat, fat reduced cocoa powder.

How many additives are there in this gateau? An additive is shown by the letter E, followed by a number.

Questions

1 Why are additives put in food?

2 Why do some people avoid food that contains additives?

3 Have a competition to see who can find the food containing the most additives. (Look on the labels of food packets and tins)

6·4 Teeth

Teeth grow out of holes called **sockets** in your jaw bone. Before digestion starts teeth are used for biting and chewing food.

Enamel forms the hard, biting surface of a tooth.

Dentine is similar to bone.

The **pulp cavity** contains nerve endings and blood vessels.

Cement holds the tooth in its socket.

Gum

Tooth decay starts on the top of large back teeth, and where one tooth touches another.

Gum disease starts between the gum and teeth. It can destroy tooth cement and cause teeth to fall out.

Why teeth decay

Tooth decay happens when the **bacteria** in your mouth turn the **sugar** in your food into **acid**. The acid eats a hole in tooth enamel and dentine. When the hole reaches a nerve you get toothache.

Gum disease

If you don't clean your teeth regularly they become covered with a layer of food and bacteria called **plaque**. Gum disease starts if the plaque gets between the gum and a tooth. The plaque rots and causes the gum to swell and bleed.

Preventing tooth decay and gum disease

1 Eat less sugary foods, because **sugar** + **bacteria** = **acid** which rots teeth.

2 Brush your teeth at least once a day to remove plaque.

3 Use fluoride toothpaste. Fluoride strengthens tooth enamel.

4 Visit a dentist every six months.

. . .so don't forget to brush your teeth!

. . .so don't forget to brush your teeth!!

Questions

1 What is plaque?

2 How does plaque cause tooth decay and gum disease?

3 Why should you use fluoride tooth paste?

4 Name three foods which can rot your teeth. Explain why in each case.

6.5 Digestion

Bread and bacon and rice and all the other things you eat must be changed into a liquid inside your body, before your body can use them. The breaking down of food into a liquid is called **digestion**.

Food is digested inside a tube in your body called the gut, or **alimentary canal**. Your alimentary canal is over seven metres long and coiled inside your body.

No matter what you eat, it is turned into liquid in your gut.

Where your food is digested

Digestion starts when food is taken into the mouth. This is called **ingestion**. The teeth are used to break the food into small pieces. The pieces are mixed with a liquid called **saliva** and swallowed.

The walls of the gut produce chemicals called **digestive enzymes**. Enzymes break down food into liquids.

Liquid food passes through the gut wall into the blood stream. This is called **absorption**. Blood carries food to all parts of the body.

Food is taken in by cells, and used for energy, growth, and repair. This is called **assimilation**.

Dietary fibre and other things in food which cannot be digested pass out through the anus when you visit the toilet. This is called **defecation**.

Substances which cannot be digested are called **faeces**.

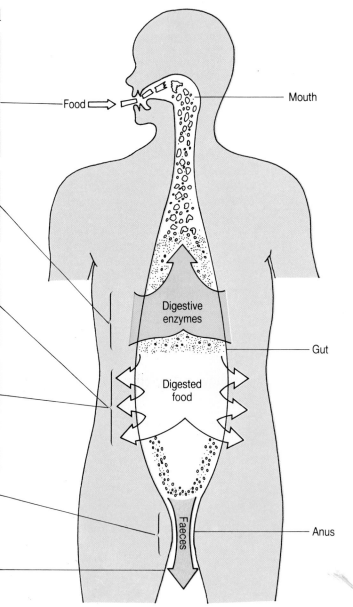

114

More about digestive enzymes

Digestive enzymes change the food you eat by breaking down large food molecules into smaller ones which can be absorbed into the blood. Each type of food needs a different enzyme to break it down.

Amylase enzymes break down carbohydrates like starch into glucose.

Lipase enzymes break down fats and oils into fatty acids and glycerol.

Protease enzymes break down proteins into amino acids.

This is what happens when starch is broken down by amylase enzyme and absorbed.

Starch is a carbohydrate found in rice, bread, and potatoes. Starch molecules are made up of many glucose molecules joined together, like a string of beads.

Amylase enzymes break down the starch by cutting it up into separate glucose molecules, like you might cut up a string of beads with scissors.

Glucose molecules are so small that they can pass through the cells which form the gut wall, and then through blood vessel walls into the blood stream.

Blood carries the glucose to the cells of the body for assimilation.

Other kinds of food are broken down by other enzymes in the same way.

Starch molecule (many glucose molecules joined together)

ENZYME
ENZYME
ENZYME

Amylase enzymes cut starch up into glucose molecules

Glucose molecules

Cells of gut wall

Glucose in blood stream

Questions

1 What is your alimentary canal?
2 What is the scientific word for:
   a) taking food into your mouth?
   b) breaking down food into small molecules?
   c) movement of food molecules into the blood?

   d) getting rid of undigested food?
3 Name the enzymes which digest: protein, carbohydrates, fats.
4 Which of the foods in question 3 are digested into: amino acids? glucose? fatty acids and glycerol?

6·6 A closer look at digestion

Digestion in the mouth

Digestion starts in your mouth. When you chew, food is ground into a pulp. At the same time, it is mixed with **saliva** from salivary glands. Saliva does two main things:

1   It wets the food, so that it slips easily down your throat.

2   It contains an **amylase enzyme** which starts to digest the starch in your food into sugar.

Salivary glands in the cheeks and under the tongue.

Swallowing

Before you swallow food, your tongue shapes it into a round lump called a **bolus**, and squeezes it to the back of your mouth.

The bolus pushes the **soft palate** upwards. This stops food getting into the space behind your nose.

A flap of skin called the **epiglottis** drops over the top of the wind-pipe. This stops food getting into your lungs.

The bolus is squeezed past the epiglottis, into your gullet or **oesophagus**.

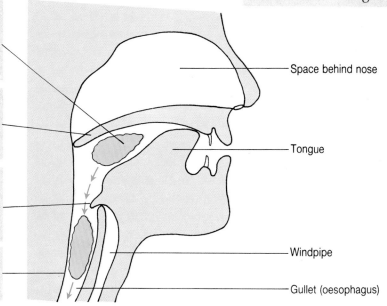

Space behind nose

Tongue

Windpipe

Gullet (oesophagus)

How food moves along the alimentary canal

Your gullet, and the rest of your alimentary canal, has **circular muscles** in its walls.

These muscles contract behind a bolus, and relax in front of it. So the bolus gets pushed along.

This contraction and relaxation of circular muscles is called **peristalsis**. It takes place all the way along your alimentary canal, and keeps food moving.

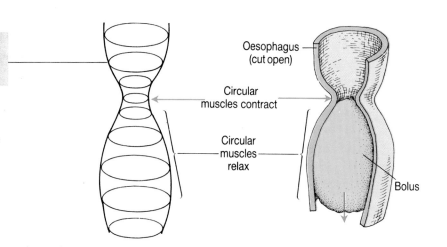

Oesophagus (cut open)

Circular muscles contract

Circular muscles relax

Bolus

Digestion in the stomach and intestine

This is a simplified diagram of the alimentary canal. The drawing on page 102 shows what it really looks like, and its position in the body.

1 From the gullet, food passes to the **stomach**. Stomach muscles squeeze and relax mixing the food with **gastric juice** and **acid** made in the stomach wall. Gastric juice contains **protease enzymes** to digest protein. The acid kills germs in food and helps the enzyme work.

Liver

Gullet (oesophagus)

2 From the stomach, the food passes a little at a time into the **small intestine**.

In the small intestine three liquids are mixed with the food:

i pancreatic juice from the pancreas. It contains a mixture of enzymes which continue to digest the food

3 Digested food is absorbed into the blood through the wall of the **small intestine**.

ii bile from the liver. It breaks up oil droplets to make them easier to digest. It also neutralizes stomach acid to get the food ready for more enzymes.

4 Undigested food passes into the **colon** where water is absorbed from it. It becomes a nearly solid waste called **faeces**.

iii intestinal juice from the lining of the intestine. This juice contains enzymes which complete digestion.

5 Faeces are stored in the **rectum**.

6 Faeces pass out of the body through the **anus** when you go to the toilet.

Questions

1 Where in your body does digestion begin?
2 What are salivary glands for?
3 What might happen if you had no epiglottis?

4 What is the scientific name for your gut?
5 What substances are mixed with food in your stomach? How does each help digestion?

Absorption, and the liver

Digestion breaks down food so it can be absorbed into your blood and carried to all parts of your body. Carbohydrates are digested into glucose, proteins into amino acids, and fats and oils into fatty acids and glycerol. But vitamins, minerals, and water in food don't have to be digested since they are already easily absorbed.

Digested foods are absorbed through your gut wall into the blood and carried away. Most absorption goes on in your small intestine.

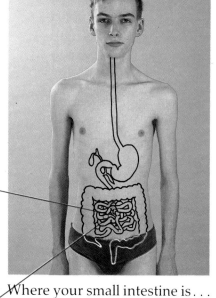

Inside the small intestine

Your small intestine is over six metres long. Inside, millions of tiny fingers called **villi** stick out of its walls. One villus is about a millimetre long.

Absorption takes place through the villi. They provide a large surface for absorbing digested food.

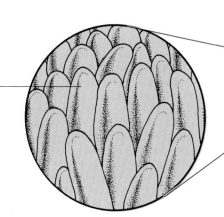

Where your small intestine is . . .
It extends down from your waist.

Inside a villus

A villus has a surface layer only one cell thick. This lets digested food pass through easily.

It has a network of **capillaries** which carry blood.

It has a lymph vessel called a **lacteal** which carries lymph.

Glucose, amino acids, and some fatty acids and glycerol pass into the blood in the capillaries. Blood carries them to the liver, which is described on the next page.

Most of the fatty acids and glycerol pass into the lacteal. They are carried in the lymph to a vein in the neck. From there they flow into the blood and are carried to all parts of the body.

Blood vessel carrying digested food to the liver.

Lymph vessel carrying digested food to the blood stream.

What happens to digested food in the liver

Your liver is the largest organ in your body. It weighs over one kilogram and stretches all the way across your body, just above the waist.

The liver is a chemical factory, a food store, and a central heating system. Here are just a few of the jobs it does:

1 It stores glucose as **glycogen**. It changes this back to glucose when the body needs it.

2 It stores the minerals copper and potassium, as well as iron needed to make red blood cells.

3 It stores vitamins A, B, and D.

4 It takes the goodness out of unwanted amino acids, and changes what is left into a waste called **urea**. Urea is removed from your body by your kidneys.

5 It takes some poisons from the blood and makes them harmless. These poisons come from germs, alcohol, and drugs.

6 It makes **bile**, which is needed for digestion.

7 It makes **fibrinogen**, which is needed for blood to clot in wounds.

8 These and many other jobs done in the liver produce heat, which the blood carries around your body to keep it warm.

Glucose, amino acids, vitamins, minerals, and some fatty acids and glycerol are absorbed into the villi.

Villus

Bile

Blood to the gut

Blood full of digested food goes to the liver

The liver

Food storage

VITAMINS GLYCOGEN MINERALS SUGAR

Chemical factory

FOOD

CHEMICALS

Heat production

HEAT

Questions

1 Digested food is absorbed inside your body. What does that mean?

2 Think of a reason why food has to be digested before it can be absorbed.

3 Where in your body are villi? What are they for?

4 Where in your body is your liver?

5 Name three things stored in your liver.

6 How does your liver help give you a steady supply of glucose?

7 Explain how:
   a) your liver helps digestion
   b) your liver helps cuts to stop bleeding
   c) your liver keeps you warm.

6·8 Biotechnology

Both of the photographs below show chemical factories. But the shapes on the right do not look like factories. In fact they are **microbes**. Microbes are tiny living things that can only be seen using a microscope. The microbes in the photograph are **bacteria**, and scientists use them to make chemicals, food, fuels, medicines, and even plastics. Just like a factory.

This chemical factory covers several thousand square metres.

...while these are so small that 200 placed end-to-end would fit across this full stop.

Biotechnology

Biotechnology means using microbes and other living things to do jobs for us, and make things we want. For centuries we have used bacteria to make cheese and yoghurt from milk, and other microbes called **yeast** to make bread, beer, and wine.

This diagram shows the many ways that microbes can be used. Because they can produce foodstuff, medicines and fuel, scientists hope that microbes will help to solve the world's food, health and energy problems.

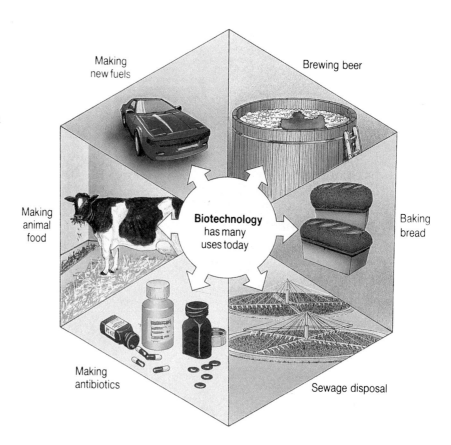

Making new fuels

Brewing beer

Making animal food

Biotechnology has many uses today

Baking bread

Making antibiotics

Sewage disposal

Modern biotechnology

These days biotechnology helps us in many ways.

Medicine. A very powerful medicine called **penicillin** was discovered in 1928. Penicillin is produced by a microbe called a fungus. It is an **antibiotic** which means it kills germs inside the human body.

Food from crude oil. There are microbes that live on cheap chemicals found in crude oil. They form a thick broth which can be dried and compressed to make protein food for animals.

Food from water. Microbes called algae grow in water containing dissolved minerals. They can be used to produce unlimited amounts of proteins, vitamins, and other useful substances for a hungry world.

Gas and fertilizers from sewage. Modern sewage disposal plants use microbes to change sewage into fertilizer. Microbes are used to digest sewage, and animal waste from farms, to produce methane gas. This can be used as fuel in factories and homes.

Antibiotics are tested on plates of germs. If an antibiotic is effective it kills a wide radius of germs.

All these antibiotics have been made by microbes.

Genetic engineering

Scientists can make microbes and other organisms produce useful things by changing their genes. This is called **genetic engineering**.

Genes can be transferred from human cells to the plasmids (or gene circles) of bacteria. The genes then work as if they were still in the human cells.

If a gene which controls the production of a human hormone is put into a bacterium, the bacterium becomes a tiny hormone factory.

In this way, bacteria have been used to produce human growth hormones for children who do not grow properly, human insulin for diabetics, and vaccines and vitamins.

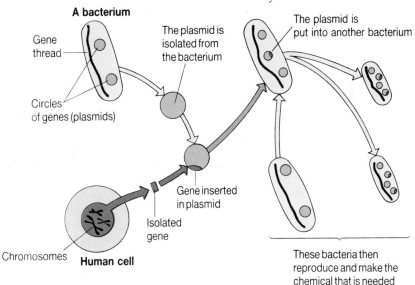

Questions

1 What are microbes? Give two examples.

2 What does biotechnology mean?

3 What are the oldest examples of biotechnology?

4 How could biotechnology help solve the world's food shortage problems?

5 a) What is genetic engineering?
  b) How can we benefit from it?

Food energy and composition

Food and energy

All foods except vitamins and minerals contain stored energy. This energy is released and made available to living things during the chemical reactions of respiration (Unit 4.4).

When food is burned it releases the same amount of energy, in the form of heat, as it does when respired. To discover the energy value of food it is burned in a **calorimeter**. All the heat given off by the food is transferred to a known quantity of water, which rises in temperature. It takes 4.2 joules of heat to raise the temperature of 1g of water by 1°C. So the energy value of food is calculated by the formula: temperature rise × 4.2 × mass of water. A food's energy value is usually quoted in **kilojoules**: 1 kilojoule (1 kJ) = 1000 joules.

These measurements give the *potential* rather than the *actual* energy value of a food. If you eat bread and butter, whose energy value is 1000 kJ, you do not get 1000 kJ of energy. First, the bran in bread and some of the fat in butter passes undigested through the gut so its energy is lost. Second, up to 85 per cent of the energy is lost as heat. Study the text opposite before reading further.

1 Popular books and magazines quote energy values in Calories. 1 Calorie = 4.2 kJ. Change the energy values in the question below into Calories.
2 Study these energy values per 100 g of food.
    butter .... 3006 kJ
    wholemeal bread .... 1025 kJ
    glucose sugar .... 1685 kJ
a) Which is a source of instant energy? Explain your answer.
b) One of these will yield about 15 per cent of the energy quoted above in respiration, the others will yield less. Which is which? Explain your answer.

Types of food and their composition

The six types of food are: carbohydrates, proteins, fats and oils, minerals and vitamins.

Carbohydrates. These are found in sugary and starchy foods such as sweet fruits, honey, jam, bread, cakes, potatoes, rice and spaghetti. Carbohydrates are the main source of energy for living things. One gram yields about 17kJ of energy during respiration. Most carbohydrates are converted by the body into glucose before they are respired.

Plants store large quantities of starch in their seeds and in storage organs like potato tubers. In animals the main carbohydrate food reserve is **glycogen** which is similar to starch. Animals can store only limited amounts of glycogen, and when this limit is exceeded any excess carbohydrate in the diet is changed into fat or oil and stored in the body.

1 Sort these foods into
a) those mostly carbohydrate, protein, or fat,
b) those with a mixture of these foods.
2 For b) above, find out how much of each type of food these items contain.

Fats and oils. These are also known as **lipids** and include butter, lard, suet, dripping, and olive and codliver oil. These are important sources of energy because 1 g of lipid can yield up to 38 kJ of energy when respired. But they are less easily digested than other foods, which reduces their energy value a little.

Fats are very important food reserves in animals and plants. First, because their high energy yield means they are less bulky than other foods, and second because layers of fatty tissue, especially under the skin of animals, insulate the body against loss of heat.

Proteins. The most important sources of protein are meat, liver, kidney, eggs, fish and beans. These foods supply the raw materials living things need for growth, and for repair of damaged and worn-out tissue. Proteins are not usually respired for energy, but when this happens they can yield up to 17 kJ of energy per gram.

Proteins are digested into chemicals called **amino acids**. There are about twenty-six of these but only ten, called the **essential amino acids** are needed by humans. Our bodies can make the rest. Animal proteins contain all ten essential amino acids, and so are called **first-class proteins**.

This child is suffering from **marasmus** – a condition caused by lack of protein.

Vegetarian diets and protein deficiency. No single plant protein contains all the essential amino acids, and so they are called **second-class proteins**. However, all ten can be obtained by eating a wide variety of plant foods.

A vegetarian diet can be extremely healthy because it does not usually contain excessive amounts of fat, sugar or salt, and is high in dietary fibre.

Vitamins. Vitamins are substances with no energy value, but which are essential for growth and health. Some are needed in very small amounts – less than one millionth of a gram a day.

There are thirteen major vitamins. They take part in the chemical reactions of metabolism, usually in conjunction with enzymes. Shortage of vitamins in the diet causes diseases described in Unit 6.1.

Minerals. You require about fifteen different minerals in your diet. Like vitamins they have no energy value but are essential for health. Most essential minerals are supplied by a diet of meat, eggs, milk, green vegetables and fruit (Unit 6.1).

Copy the chart on the right and fill it in using information in this unit and in Unit 6.1.

	Carbohydrates	Fats and oils	Proteins	Vitamins	Minerals
Fried cod					
Orange juice					
Prevents rickets					
Toffee					
Fish and chips					
Body-building food					
Liver					
Heal wounds					
For strong bones					
Milk chocolate					
Contains amino acids					

6·B Nutrition and health

Study the graph and text opposite before reading this unit.

1 The Seventh Day Adventists are a religious sect based mainly in the USA. They never smoke, or drink alcohol, and eat a mainly vegetarian diet with a little meat and dairy produce.

2 Use these facts and the graph opposite to formulate hypotheses to account for their remarkable health record, compared with the general population.

Malnutrition

This means bad nutrition, but the word usually refers to the effects on the body of eating too much, too little, or the wrong kinds of food.

Eating too much

You are eating too much if the energy value of the food you eat each day exceeds the amount of energy you use in that time (unit 6.2). Eating too much can lead to weight increase (obesity).

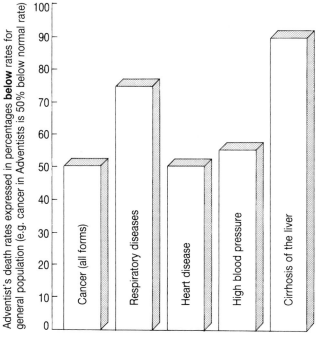

There is now clear evidence that obesity contributes to heart disease, high blood pressure, diabetes, gall bladder disease, cancer of the bowel, and breast and womb cancer in women.

What does the graph opposite tell you about the dangers of obesity in men and women?

Eating too much of the wrong kinds of food, such as fatty, sugary and salty foods is especially dangerous.

Eating too much fat. Excess animal fat in the diet is dangerous because it leads to the formation of cholesterol (unit 5.3). It has also been estimated that diets high in animal fats cause one third of all cancers.

Remember that, in addition to butter, cream and fatty meat, there is much hidden fat in burgers, sausages, crisps, peanuts and chocolate. Study the text below before reading further.

*Compare these figures. Five chocolate biscuits (about 100 g) supply enough energy for a man to cycle for 87 minutes at 15 kph. The **same weight** of wholemeal bread supplies only enough energy for 36 minutes' cycling at this speed. What has this got to do with the following statements.*
'Some foods supply all your daily energy needs long before they satisfy your appetite.'
'It is easy to eat too much without realizing it.'

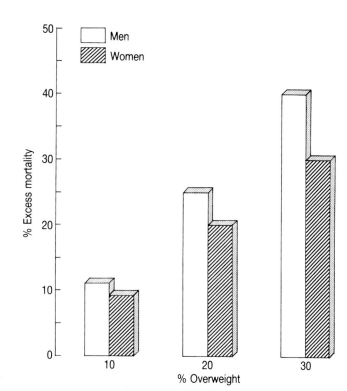

Eating too much sugar. Sugar causes tooth decay (Unit 6.4), and is linked with diabetes. It can also cause obesity because you can eat a lot without feeling full. Ice-cream and chocolate are among the most fattening foods because they contain both sugar and fat.

Eating too much salt. There is evidence which links high salt intake with high blood pressure, a major factor in heart disease and strokes, and with stomach cancer. On average the British eat 2.5 teaspoons of salt daily (12 g). About 88 per cent of this is already present in food, especially factory made (processed) foods (see graph). Cut down on salt by adding less to food, and eating fewer packet soups, foods preserved in brine, bacon and salted potato crisps.

Dietary fibre (roughage)

Fibre is the bran of cereals and the cellulose walls of plant cells, which pass unchanged through the gut because they are not digested.

High fibre foods. Wholemeal products contain up to 8.5 per cent more bran than white flour products. Bran breakfast cereals are 25 per cent bran. Other high fibre foods are potatoes in their skins, berries, nuts, bananas, apples, oranges and vegetables such as sweetcorn, spinach and broccoli. Study the text opposite before reading further.

Why fibre is important. When populations with high and low fibre diets are compared it is found that those with low fibre diets are more likely to suffer from constipation, heart disease, diabetes, and cancer of the bowel. Some reasons for this are:

1 Low fibre food passes slowly through the gut and forms lumps which stick and cause constipation. High fibre foods have more bulk, which allows gut muscles to grip and move them along by peristalsis.

2 Fibre absorbs poisonous wastes from digesting food.

3 Fibre helps avoid obesity by adding indigestible matter to food. This satisfies your appetite but can't make you fat.

Sensible slimming

Study the graph and text opposite.

Despite what clever advertisements tell you, there is no way to lose weight except by reducing your daily energy input (food) so it is below your energy output (the energy you use up each day). Exercise helps by raising energy output, and it also makes you feel fitter and more healthy.

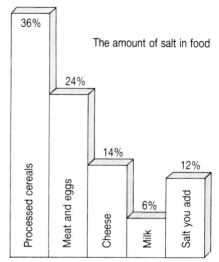

The amount of salt in food

1 Hypothesis: a high fibre diet helps keep you slim.

2 Study what has been said so far about low fibre foods (e.g. meat and dairy produce) and the definition of dietary fibre, then list the evidence in support of this hypothesis.

*1 An 'energy gap' is caused by eating a daily ration of food with a **smaller** energy value than the energy you expend each day (see table in Unit 6.2).*

*2 A = an energy gap of 2100 kJ (500 Calories).
B = an energy gap of 2900 kJ (700 Calories).
C = an energy gap of 4200 kJ (1000 Calories).*

3 Account for the weight losses shown in the graph. What effect would extra exercise (e.g. jogging) have on the energy gap, and weight loss?

125

1 Recall knowledge
Copy the following sentences into your exercise book. Then fill in the gaps using words from the list: **carbohydrates, proteins, fats and oils, vitamins and minerals, dietary fibre**.

a) .... are body-building foods.
b) Foods rich in .... are stored in your body to provde energy in the future.
c) You need .... to avoid constipation.
d) Food rich in .... provides energy quickly.
e) You need about twenty different .... to stay healthy.
f) Starch and sugar are examples of ....
g) Fresh fruit contains plenty of ....
h) Wholemeal bread contains plenty of ....
i) Eggs and fish are rich in ....
j) Butter is rich in ....

2 Recall knowledge
a) Write down three headings: *Rich in proteins, Rich in carbohydrates, Rich in fats*.
b) Now sort this list of food into three groups under these headings:
jam, lean ham, peanuts, toffee, lard, cake, chicken, egg, butter, potato, fish.

3 Recall knowledge
Copy these sentences, then fill in the gaps.
a) ..... and Vitamin ..... are needed for strong bones and teeth.
b) Vitamin ..... is needed to heal wounds quickly.
c) ..... is needed for making red blood cells.
d) Lack of Vitamin ..... causes scurvy.
e) Lack of Vitamin ..... causes rickets.
f) Lack of ..... causes anaemia.

4 Recall knowledge
Instant mashed potato is an example of a processed food. To make it, potatoes are put through special processes in a factory.
a) What good things may be taken out of food when it is processed?
b) Name three types of food additives which may be added to food during processing.

c) Why are these chemicals added to food?
d) Think of four reasons why people buy processed foods.
e) Think of four reasons why it is better to buy fresh foods than processed foods.
f) What is the difference between:
wholemeal bread and white bread?
juice from a crushed orange and an orange-flavoured drink?
garden peas and tinned peas?
roast jacket potato and instant potato?

5 Recall knowledge
Below is a diagram of the digestive system.
a) Name the parts labelled A to J.
b) Match the labels on the diagram with the descriptions below:
where digested food passes into the blood stream;
where food is mixed with gastric juice;
where faeces leave the body;
a gland which produces enzymes that digest protein, starch, and fat;
glands which produce saliva;
where water is absorbed from the undigested remains of food;
pumps bile into the small intestine;
stores glycogen, vitamins, and minerals.

6 *Understanding/evaluation/design*
A group of students designed the experiment opposite to find the energy value of peanuts.

a) Their result was 1900kJ per 100g of peanuts.

b) How was the apparatus used to obtain this result?

c) Official tables give the energy value of peanuts as 2445kJ per 100g. Give two reasons why the students obtained a lower result.

d) Redesign the method to improve the accuracy of the result.

e) The students decided to use this method to find the energy value of bread. Which experimental conditions must they keep the same so that results can be compared with those for peanuts?

7 *Interpret data*
A dish was filled with a jelly (agar) containing starch. Five cavities were cut in the surface of the jelly, and each was filled with a different liquid (see diagram opposite). The apparatus was kept warm for an hour then flooded with iodine solution. The result is shown in the diagram opposite.

a) How does iodine affect starch?

b) Describe three things this result tells you about saliva.

c) Is it possible to say that wheat grains contain a substance similar to saliva? If they do, what use could it be during germination?

8 *Understanding/interpret data*
The chart opposite shows the average amount of energy which British and Japanese people obtain from various foods.

a) Cereals and meat are sources of protein. Which also contains the most fibre, and which contains the most fat?

b) How much more meat, fat and oil do the British eat than the Japanese?

c) Low fibre, high fat diet can cause heart disease. Would you expect heart disease to be less common in Japan or in Britain? Explain your answer.

d) Would you expect tooth decay to be less common in Britain or Japan? Explain your answer.

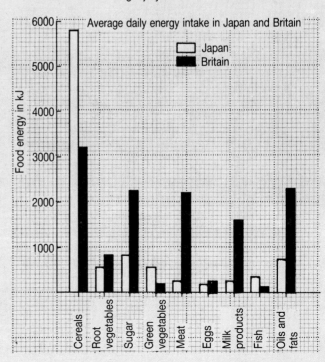

7

7·1 Touch, taste, and smell

You can touch, taste, smell, hear, balance, and see because of your sense organs. In humans the sense organs are:

1 The **skin**, which is sensitive to pressure, heat, and cold and gives you your sense of touch.
2 The **tongue**, which is sensitive to chemicals in food and drink, and gives you your sense of taste.
3 The **nose**, which is sensitive to chemicals in the air, and gives you your sense of smell.
4 The **ears**, which are sensitive to sounds and movement, and give you your senses of hearing and balance.
5 The **eyes**, which are sensitive to light, and give you your sense of sight.

When a sense organ detects a **stimulus** such as sound or light, it sends messages along nerves to the brain. The brain then gives you feelings or **sensations** such as hearing or sight.

A cat has a special set of sense organs – its whiskers. They are the same width as the cat's body. It uses them to judge whether it can squeeze through a gap.

The skin

Your sense of touch is produced by the ends of nerve cells in your skin. These are called **nerve endings**.

These nerve endings deep inside the skin are sensitive to heavy pressure. They warn you about pressure which could bruise you.

These nerve endings near the skin surface are sensitive to light pressure. They tell you about the texture of an object, for example whether it is rough or smooth.

These nerve endings very close to the skin surface make you feel pain if, for example, your skin is cut or burnt.

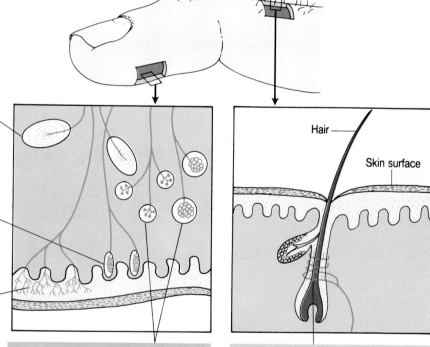

These nerve endings are sensitive to heat and cold. They detect changes in temperature. For example, when the weather changes, or when you touch cold or hot objects.

These nerve endings wrapped around the base of a hair detect if the hair is moved or pulled.

The tongue

Your tongue has little bumps on it. These bumps contain tiny sense organs called **taste buds**. Taste buds are sensitive to chemicals in food. These chemicals must dissolve in saliva before you can taste them. This is why dry food has no taste until you chew it to mix it with saliva.

Your sense of taste is useful.
1   It stimulates your stomach to produce gastric juice for digestion.
2   Many poisons and bad foods have a nasty taste. So you can spit them out before they harm you.

There are different taste buds for tasting bitter, sour, salty, and sweet foods.

A food can stimulate more than one kind of taste bud at the same time.

The taste buds for **bitter tastes** are at the back of your tongue.

The taste buds for **sour tastes** are at the sides of your tongue.

The taste buds for **salty and sweet** tastes are at the front of your tongue.

The nose

When a bad cold blocks your nose, food seems to lose its flavour. This is because many flavours are really smells!

Smells are chemicals in the air. The chemicals dissolve in moisture on the lining of your nose. This stimulates nerve endings in your nose to send messages to your brain which produces the sensation of smell.

Humans can detect about 3000 different smells. Smells help animals to hunt food and find their way. Smells can also warn of certain dangers.

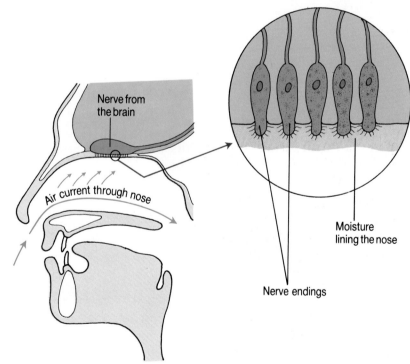

Nerve from the brain

Air current through nose

Moisture lining the nose

Nerve endings

Questions

1   Name the five sense organs in humans.
2   If you gently stroke the hairs on your arm you feel a tingling sensation. Try to explain why.
3   Why do foods seem to have less flavour when you have a cold in the nose?
4   How do taste and smell protect you?

How you see things

1 Light goes from an object to your eye.

2 Light is bent as it passes through your eye.

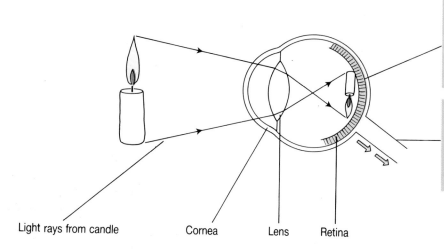

3 An upside-down picture of the object is focused on a layer called the **retina** at the back of your eye. The retina is made of cells sensitive to light.

4 The retina sends messages along the **optic nerve** to your brain. Your brain allows you to see a picture of the object which is the right way up.

Light rays from candle   Cornea   Lens   Retina

How eyes are protected

Your eyes are set in holes called **orbits** in your skull. So all except the front of each eye is protected by bone.

There are **tear glands** behind the top eyelid. They make tears that wash your eye clean when you blink. Tears are produced faster if dust or smoke get into your eyes.

The **iris** is the coloured part of the eye. It is a ring of muscle with a hole called the pupil in the middle. It protects the eyes from bright light.

Eyelashes form a net in front of the eye which protects it from dust.

The white of the eye is a tough protective layer called the **sclerotic.**

The **pupil** lets light into the eye. If the light is too bright the iris muscle makes the pupil smaller. In dim light the iris muscle make the pupil bigger.

The parts of the eye

The **conjunctiva** is a thin clear skin which covers the front of the eye.

The **cornea** is a clear window in the sclerotic in front of the iris. It lets light into the eye.

The **iris** controls the amount of light entering the eye.

The front part of the eye is filled with a watery liquid called **aqueous humour**.

The **lens** helps focus a picture on the retina. The lens is clear and can change shape.

The **suspensory ligaments** hold the lens in place.

The **sclerotic layer** is the tough, white protective layer of the eye.

The back of the eye is filled with a jelly called **vitreous humour**.

The **choroid** is a black layer that stops light being reflected round the inside of the eye.

Ciliary muscles change the shape of the lens during focusing.

The **yellow spot** is the most sensitive part of the retina. It lets you see colour.

Optic nerve

The **retina** is a layer of cells which are sensitive to light. They send messages to the brain.

The **blind spot** is where blood vessels and nerves join the eyeball. It has no light-sensitive cells, so it sends no messages to the brain.

Questions

1 Give the scientific name for each of these:
   a) carries messages from an eye to the brain.
   b) muscles which change the shape of a lens.
   c) A layer of light-sensitive cells.
   d) It controls the amount of light entering the eye.
   e) It prevents light being reflected around the eye.
   f) They make liquid which washes the eyes.
   g) A hole in the middle of the iris.
   h) A clear window at the front of the eye.
   i) changes shape to focus a picture on the retina.

2 If you walk from a dark room into sunlight and back again how would your pupils alter in size? Why does this happen?

7.3 Vision

The light that goes into your eye has to be bent or **focused** onto the retina to let you see clearly.

Most of the bending of light takes place as it passes through the **cornea** and **aqueous humour**. The **lens** bends it a little more to make a perfectly clear picture on the retina. The **ciliary muscles** change the shape of the lens to bend light. A fat lens bends light more than a thin lens.

If the lenses in your eyes don't focus properly, wearing glasses will help

To see a distant object

Light from a distant object needs to be bent very little. So the lens is stretched to make it thin.

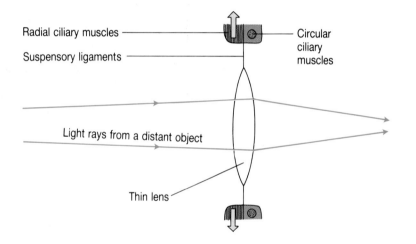

1 The **radial ciliary muscles** contract and pull against the edges of the lens.

2 This stretches the lens making it thin and flat. So it bends light just a little, to make a clear picture on the retina.

To see a near object

Light from a near object needs to be bent more than light from a distant object. So the lens is made much fatter.

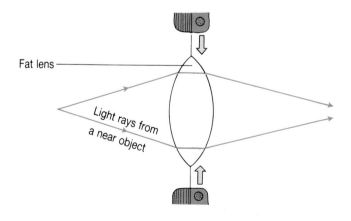

1 The ciliary muscles are in a circle round the eyeball. They contract and squeeze the eyeball inwards.

2 The lens becomes much fatter in shape. Now it can bend light enough to make a clear picture on the retina.

Three dimensional vision

Each of your eyes gets a slightly different view of an object.

Your brain puts these two views together, so that you see the object as three-dimensional rather than flat.

Three-dimensional vision helps you judge how far away an object is.

The left eye sees this view

The right eye sees this view

Two eyes

Rabbits, chickens, fish, and many other animals have eyes which look sideways, and not forwards like yours. Each eye sees a different view. They can even see what is happening behind them. This is useful if other animals hunt you for food!

Rabbits can see what's going on at each side . . .

. . . but owls look straight ahead.

More about the retina

There are two kinds of light-sensitive cells in the retina. They are called **rods** and **cones**.

Cones only work in bright light, but give a very clear picture and are sensitive to colour. The **yellow spot** in the middle of the retina is made entirely of cones.

If you want to see something very clearly you look straight at it, so that its picture falls on the yellow spot.

The rest of the retina is mostly rods, with a few cones. Rods do not give as clear a picture as cones and are not sensitive to colour. But rods work in dim light.

This explains why you don't see colours clearly in dim light.

Questions

1 Which parts of an eye bend light?

2 What shape are your eye lenses when you look at your hand? What shape are they when you look at a tree in the distance?

3 **a)** Where in the retina are rods and cones found?

   b) Which detect colour, and which work in dim light?

Ears, hearing and balance

The air around you is full of vibrations called **sound waves**. You do not hear sound waves with your ears. You 'hear' them inside your brain. This is what happens.

Sound waves move through the air at 332 metres per second from bells, radios, birds, cars and so on. When they reach your ear they are changed into 'messages' called **nerve impulses**.

Nerve impulses travel along a nerve from each ear to your brain. Your brain transforms them into a sensation of sound.

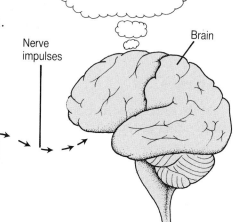

Thinks: 'Who's making all that noise?'

Brain

Nerve impulses

Sound waves

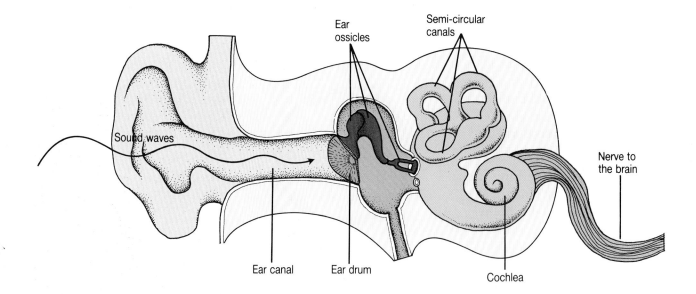

Ear ossicles

Semi-circular canals

Sound waves

Nerve to the brain

Ear canal   Ear drum

Cochlea

The part which you call your ear is a flap of skin in the shape of a funnel. This leads to a tunnel, the **ear canal** into your head. Sound waves are collected by the funnel. They move down the ear canal to a thin sheet of skin called the **ear drum**.

The ear drum is connected to the inner ear by three tiny bones called **ear ossicles**. The part of the inner ear concerned with hearing is called the **cochlea**. It is coiled like the shell of a snail.

How the ear works

This diagram shows the cochlea straightened out.

1 Sound waves make the ear drum vibrate in and out. This makes the ossicles vibrate.
2 The ossicles are connected to another sheet of skin called the **oval window**. When the ossicles vibrate they make the oval window vibrate in and out.

3 When the oval window moves in and out it causes vibrations to move through the cochlea.
4 The cochlea contains a carpet of tiny hairs which are connected to nerves. Vibrations in the cochlea cause these hairs to vibrate up and down and send impulses to the brain where we hear the sounds.

Keeping your balance

You keep your balance in two ways. Your eyes tell you if you are upright or tilted. The semi-circular canals of your inner ears tell you if you are moving off balance.

The semi-circular canals are shown in the diagram on the opposite page. They are three tubes full of liquid. When you move the liquid moves. Sensitive hairs inside the tubes detect this movement and send impulses along nerves to your brain. Your brain detects when you are losing your balance and sends impulses to muscles to keep you upright.

Questions

1 Which part of your ear:
   a) changes vibrations into nerve impulses?
   b) keeps you from falling over?

2 Explain how the man in the photograph above keeps his balance?

Your nervous system is like a manager inside your body. Its job is to **control** and **co–ordinate** the parts of your body so that they work together, doing their jobs at the right time.

Your nervous system co-ordinates muscles so that you can do things which need thought, like cycling, dancing, or reading.

It also co-ordinates things which you don't need to think about, like heart beat and breathing.

The nervous system consists of the **brain**, the **spinal cord**, and millions of **nerves**. Together the brain and spinal cord are called the **central nervous system**.

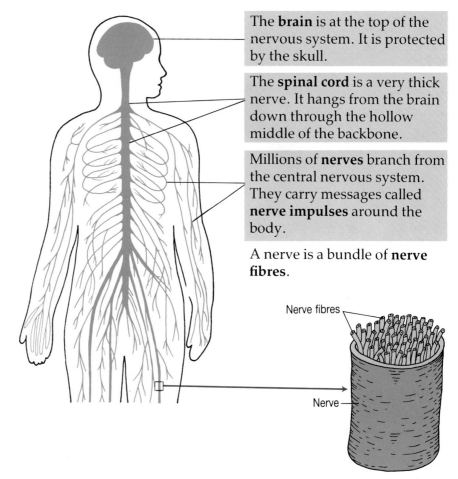

The **brain** is at the top of the nervous system. It is protected by the skull.

The **spinal cord** is a very thick nerve. It hangs from the brain down through the hollow middle of the backbone.

Millions of **nerves** branch from the central nervous system. They carry messages called **nerve impulses** around the body.

A nerve is a bundle of **nerve fibres**.

Nerve fibres

Nerve

Nerve cells

The nervous system is made up of **nerve cells**. Most cells are small and rounded. But nerve cells are not. They are stretched out into long thin **nerve fibres** that can be over a metre long. Nerve impulses travel along nerve fibres in *only one direction*.

Sensory nerve cells carry impulses from sense organs into the central nervous system.

Motor nerve cells carry impulses from the central nervous system to muscles and glands.

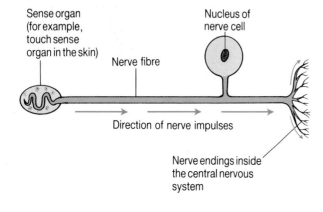

Sense organ (for example, touch sense organ in the skin)

Nucleus of nerve cell

Nerve fibre

Direction of nerve impulses

Nerve endings inside the central nervous system

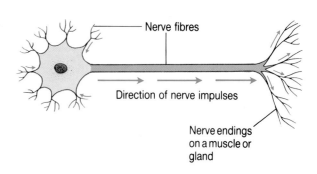

Nerve fibres

Direction of nerve impulses

Nerve endings on a muscle or gland

How the nervous system works

If you sat on a drawing pin you would jump up yelling with pain. This is an example of a **stimulus** and a **response**. The stimulus is pain. The response is jumping and yelling. Your nervous system controls the response.

This diagram of the nervous system shows how it works.

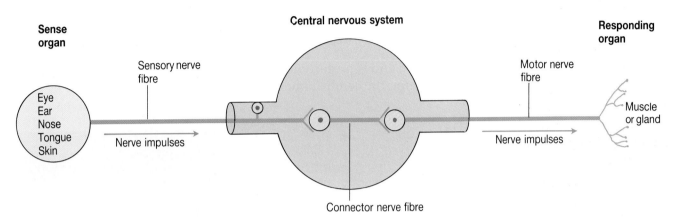

1 A stimulated sense organ sends nerve impulses along **sensory nerve fibres** to the central nervous system.

2 The central nervous system works out the best response to the stimulus. Then it sends impulses to the muscles and glands which will carry out the response.

3 The impulses travel to the muscles and glands along **motor nerve fibres**.

Reflex and voluntary actions

Reflex actions are actions you do without thinking, to protect yourself: coughing clears your windpipe, and shivering keeps you warm. The pupils get smaller in bright light, to protect the retina and larger in dull light to help you see.

Voluntary actions are actions which need thought, like speaking to a friend or writing a letter.

Questions
1 Name the parts of the nervous system.
2 Name two kinds of nerve cell.
3 How are nerve cells different from other cells?
4 What is a nerve impulse?
5 What is a reflex action?
6 What is a voluntary action?
7 Sort these into reflex and voluntary actions: coughing, reading, sneezing, sweating, writing.

7·6 The brain

There are about 10 000 million nerve cells in your brain. Each cell is linked with thousands more. This linking allows your brain to do many different jobs all at the same time.

The parts of the brain

Your brain is at the top of your spinal cord and is protected by your skull. It has three main parts: the cerebrum, the cerebellum, and the medulla.

The **cerebrum** is the dome-shaped roof of the brain.

Its **sensory areas** (blue) receive impulses from your eyes, ears, tongue, nose, and skin, and give you sensations or feelings.

Its **motor areas** (red) control your muscles during movement.

Its **association areas** (yellow) control memory and thinking.

The **medulla** controls things like heart beat, breathing, blood pressure, that go on without you having to think about them.

Nerve cells from the cerebellum of the brain. Their job is to control muscles and balance.

Your brain looks like this from above. The cerebrum is divided into two halves, called the cerebral hemispheres.

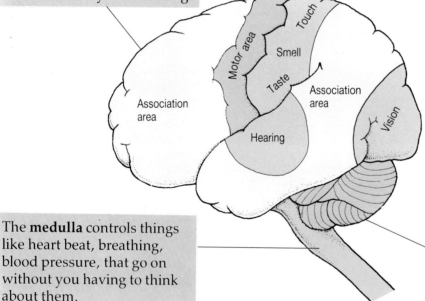

The **cerebellum** helps control your muscles and balance during walking, running, cycling, and so on.

Question

1   Which part of the brain:
   a) do you use to think?
   b) controls your breathing?
   c) helps you balance while cycling?
   d) gives you the sensation of touch?

7·7 Hormones

Hormones are made in a set of glands called the **endocrine glands**. Like the nervous system, hormones co-ordinate the body.

Endocrine glands release tiny amounts of hormones into the blood. Blood carries them all over the body, but only certain parts called **target organs** respond to them. Responses to hormones may last a few minutes, or may go on for years.

This diagram shows the main endocrine glands, the hormones they produce, and the jobs which the hormones do.

The **thyroid gland** is attached to the windpipe. It makes a hormone called **thyroxine**.

Thyroxine controls the speed of chemical reactions in cells. In children, too little thyroxine leads to slow growth and mental development.

The **adrenal glands** are on top of the kidneys. When you are angry or frightened they make a hormone called **adrenalin**.

Adrenalin prepares your body for action. It speeds up heart beat and breathing, raises blood pressure, and allows more glucose to go into the blood, to give you energy.

In females the **ovaries** make a sex hormone called **oestrogen**. Oestrogen gives girls their female features such as breasts, soft skin, and a feminine voice. It also gets the womb ready for a baby.

The **pituitary gland** is under the brain. It makes many hormones.

1 One of these hormones controls growth. A person with too little growth hormone becomes a dwarf. A person with too much becomes a giant.

2 In females, it makes hormones which control the release of eggs from ovaries, and the birth of a baby.

The **pancreas** is below the stomach. The pancreas produces a hormone called **insulin**. Insulin controls the amount of glucose in the blood. People with an illness called **diabetes** make too little insulin. So their liver releases harmful amounts of glucose into the blood.

In males the **testes** make a sex hormone called **testosterone**. This gives boys their male features such as deeper voices and more body hair than females.

Question

1 Which hormone:
   a) prepares the body for action?
   b) controls the amount of glucose in blood?
   c) gives boys a deep voice?
   d) gives girls soft skin?
   e) controls chemical reactions in cells?

7·A The senses

How many senses?

Your sense organs, or **receptors** keep you informed about what is happening outside and inside your body. How many different senses are there? Most people would name the five **special senses**: touch, taste, smell, hearing and sight. In fact there are more. Study the text opposite before reading further.

Senses inside the body

Hunger and thirst. You cannot live without food and water. There are senses which automatically keep you informed when more of these are needed. Your sense of hunger comes partly from sensory nerve endings in your stomach wall which are stimulated when your stomach contracts as it empties. When your body is short of water body fluids become more concentrated so that their **osmotic pressure** changes (see page 46). **Osmoreceptors** detect this change and a sense of thirst develops.

Muscle and joint senses.
Try the exercise opposite.

Sense organs called **stretch receptors** inside muscles and joint ligaments sense the amount of tension (stretch) in these tissues. When you bend an arm your brain can use information from its stretch receptors to put the other arm in the same position. Stretch receptors also help tell you how much you are pulling or pushing something by sensing muscle tension.

Write a list of senses other than the five listed opposite. Here are some clues:

1 How do you feel: four hours after breakfast, after a long walk on a hot day.

2 How do you know how hard you are pushing or pulling against something?

3 How do you know about the position of your arms and legs without looking?

4 How many things can you find out about objects using sense of touch alone?

5 Which sense is most important for a tight-rope walker?

1 Stand with eyes closed and arms at your sides. Raise your right arm and bend the elbow, wrist and fingers to any angle you wish (try to bend each joint to a different angle).

2 Raise your left arm and, without looking, bend its joints into exactly the same angles as your right arm. Look and see if both arms are the same. How did you do it? Which senses did you use?

Muscle fibres

Sensory nerve fibres

Stretch receptors (sensory nerve endings coiled round the muscle fibres)

'Touch' is more than one sense?

If you were blindfold and given objects to identify you could tell if they were soft or hard, rough or smooth, hot or cold, wet or dry and you could guess their weight and their shape. This is done using skin senses described in Unit 7.1. Texture and shape are judged using touch and pressure senses. Weight is judged using pressure senses and muscle stretch receptors. You cannot judge exact temperatures, only differences in temperature. The test opposite shows you how to discover more about this sense.

1 Half-fill one beaker with hot (not boiling) water, a second with ice-cold water, and a third with warm water.

2 Put your left hand in the hot water and your right hand in the ice-cold water.

3 After a minute put both hands in the warm water. How does the water feel to each hand? How does this experiment show that skin is only sensitive to differences in temperature?

Semi-circular canals and balance

The innermost part of each ear consists of three tiny curved tubes called **semi-circular canals**. Unit 7.4 explains how they work. Feel the rounded swelling behind each ear. These are skull bones which protect the canals.

The diagram opposite shows the position of one set of canals (greatly magnified) in the head. There are three canals in each set: one points fowards, another sideways and the third is horizontal. So, if you nod your head the forward-facing canal is stimulated. Whenever your head moves your brain can calculate the direction from the rate at which liquid swirls around in each canal.

Vision

How clear is the picture which your eyes give you?
Try this test before reading on.

1   Rest this book on a desk. Lower your head until it is about 20 cm from the page, close one eye and look at the 'A' opposite with the other eye.

*2   **Without moving your eye from the 'A'** try to read the other letters. How many are clearly visible? Find the yellow spot in the diagram on page 131, and try to explain this result.*

Most people find they can see only two or three letters clearly. In fact only a small part of what we see is clearly visible, all the rest is blurred. Only the area of retina immediately opposite the lens gives a clear picture. This is the **yellow spot** (Unit 7.3). But you are not normally aware of this because your eyes are rarely still, they constantly scan a scene so that all of it is eventually seen by the yellow spot.

```
                H
                G
                F
                E
                D
                C
                B
H G F E D C B   A   B C D E F G H
                B
                C
                D
                E
                F
                G
                H
```

Part of each eye is blind

Try this test before reading further.

*Hold this page at arm's length, close your **left** eye and fix the other on the black circle opposite. **Keep your eye on the circle** and bring the book towards your face. What happens to the plus sign?*

The plus sign disappears when its image falls on the **blind spot** of your right eye (see diagram on page 131). It is impossible to make the plus disappear with both eyes open because its image can never fall on the blind spot of both eyes at once. This is why you are not normally aware that you have blind spots.

7·B Co-ordination

Your muscles, heart, lungs, kidneys, digestive system and other organs do not work separately. Their work is **co-ordinated**, which means they do it at just the right times, and at just the right speed to serve the body as a whole. Study the example of co-ordination opposite.

The importance of co-ordination

Without co-ordination you would be nothing more than a collection of different organs.

To move you must contract the correct set of muscles at exactly the right moment, with the correct amount of power for the correct length of time. While this is happening your lungs and heart must be co-ordinated to deliver the correct amount of food and oxygen to your muscles and take away their wastes. At the same time your gut is digesting food, your kidneys are excreting waste along with many other co-ordinated processes throughout your body. How is all this done?

This juggler must have perfect co-ordination in order to perform his act. Which parts of his body are being co-ordinated? Which part does the co-ordinating? How does this part co-ordinate the other parts?

How organs are co-ordinated

Co-ordination is achieved in five steps:

stimulus → **sense organs** → **co-ordinators** → **effectors** → **responses**

A stimulus is anything inside or outside the body which causes a sense organ to send out nerve impulses e.g. light and sound.

Sense organs detect the stimulus, e.g. ears, eyes and nose, and senses inside the body which detect changes in blood sugar, temperature etc.

Co-ordinators are organs which receive information from sense organs and use it to control other organs throughout the body. The **brain** and **spinal cord** perform nervous co-ordination by sending out nerve impulses. **Endocrine glands** co-ordinate by sending out hormones (Unit 7.7).

Effectors are parts of the body such as muscles and glands which are controlled by co-ordinators.

Responses are what happens as a result of the stimulus e.g. leg muscles contract when you walk, lungs work faster to get more oxygen.

Nerve impulses are signals which travel along nerves. They can travel in only one direction, and a nerve must recover before it can carry another impulse, but this takes less than a thousandth of a second. How is this similar to domino toppling?

Reflexes

Answer the question opposite before reading further.

The first is a **reflex response**. It is the type of behaviour which you do automatically without thinking, and which you do not have to learn. The second is a **voluntary response**. It has to be learned and requires thought.

What is the difference between these two responses:
1   pulling your hand away from something sharp,

2   reaching out to pick something up?

Reflex arcs

Reflex responses are extremely fast because nerve impulses travel through a simple arrangement of nerves called a reflex arc. Trace the path of nerve impulses through the diagram below.

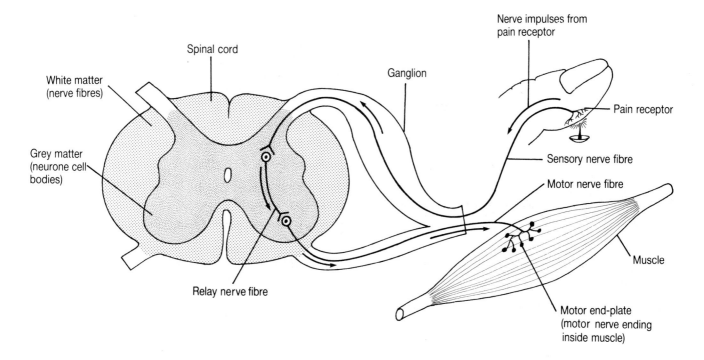

The stimulus in this example is a pricked finger. This causes impulses to travel from a **pain receptor** in the skin along a **sensory nerve fibre** to the **spinal cord**.

Here a **relay nerve fibre** carries impulses through the nerve cord to a **motor nerve fibre**. This carries impulses to **muscles** which respond by pulling the finger away. Answer the questions below.

Functions of reflexes

Many reflexes protect you from harm, like the eye-blink reflex when your eyes are in danger, or pulling away from a painful stimulus such as a sharp or hot object. Other reflexes help prevent waste. If you are hungry and smell or see delicious food your salivary glands start working – you salivate. This reflex ensures that you only produce saliva when it is needed. Similar reflexes control production of other digestive juices.

What are the functions of these two reflexes:
1   blinking your eyes if someone snaps a book shut in front of your face,

2   your mouth watering (salivation) if you are hungry and smell delicious food?

1 *Recall knowledge/understanding*

Three students were asked to sit in a row with their tongues out.

At the same moment crystals of sugar were placed on the front of the first tongue, on the sides of the next tongue, and at the back of the third one.

a) Which student was the first to taste the sugar? Explain why.

b) What will the results be if the test is repeated using salt? Using lemon juice? Using bitter-tasting instant coffee?

c) To taste food and drink properly, you should spread it all over your tongue. Explain why.

d) How do taste and smell protect us from harm?

2 *Recall knowledge*

The diagram below shows the inside of an eye.

a) Name the parts labelled A to L.

b) How does the shape of part J change: when the eye is focused on a near object? when it is focused on a distant object?

c) Describe the main differences between the parts of the eye labelled C, D, and E.

d) What happens to part I: in dim light? in bright light?

e) Describe two functions of part B.

f) What passes from the eye along part F?

3 *Understanding*

a) What is a reflex action?

b) What reflex action happens: when dust blows into your eyes? when a bright light shines in your eyes? when a very cold wind suddenly blows over you? when food 'goes the wrong way' and gets into your wind-pipe?

c) Explain how each of these reflex actions protects you from harm.

4 *Understanding/interpret data*

A group of students were asked to test the sensitivity of skin to touch. They were given pieces of cork through which two needles had been passed. In some corks the needle points were 0.5cm apart, in others they were 1.5cm apart.

While one student sat with his eyes closed another touched his skin with either one needle point or two and the student was asked if one or two points were touching his skin.

A record was made only of answers given when *two points* were used.

The students used this method on skin of the arm, palm and finger tips. The table below shows the results of 15 pairs of students. It gives the number of times each student was *correct* in judging that two needle points were touching his skin.

a) What do these results tell you about the difference in sensitivity of the arm, palms and finger tips?

b) What does it tell you about the distance apart of nerve endings in the skin which are sensitive to touch?

Distance apart at needle points	Arm	Palm	Finger tips
1.5 cm	104	155	173
0.5 cm	95	122	158

5 *Recall knowledge*

Name the glands labelled A to F on the diagram opposite, then match each label with one of these descriptions.

a) Its hormones control the speed of cell chemistry.

b) Its hormones change boys into men.

c) Its hormones control the female reproductive system.

d) Its hormones prepare the body for action.

e) Its hormones change girls into women.

f) Its hormones control the amount of glucose in blood.

6 *Recall knowledge/interpret data/understanding*

A student with one eye covered used her other eye to look at the following objects within a period of eight seconds.

A – a stationary object nearby

B – a stationary object far away

C – an object moving towards her

D – an object moving away from her

An instrument was used to measure the curvature of her lens (i.e. whether it became fatter or thinner – unit 7.3). The graph opposite shows changes in lens curvature during the eight seconds of the test.

a) Use the letters A, B, C or D to indicate which object she was looking at during the following periods

0–2 seconds,   2–4 seconds,
4–6 seconds,   6–8 seconds

b) Which set of ciliary muscles was contracted to look at object A and to look at object B?

7 *Recall knowledge/understanding*

The diagram opposite shows connections between the ear and the brain.

a) A fire alarm rings. Use letters in the diagram to indicate all the parts, in their correct sequence, involved in hearing this sound.

b) Which letters point to the part(s) that:
are a set of three small bones;
changes sound vibrations into nerve impulses;
interpret nerve impulses as sounds.

c) What part do B, H and G play when you run for safety?

Two kinds of reproduction

Reproduction is the creation of new living things. There are two ways it can happen: by **asexual reproduction**, or by **sexual reproduction**.

Asexual reproduction

In asexual reproduction there is only one parent. Most tiny simple organisms reproduce in this way.

Tiny creatures like *Amoeba* and *Paramecium* are made up of only one cell. They reproduce asexually in the simplest possible way, by dividing to form two cells.

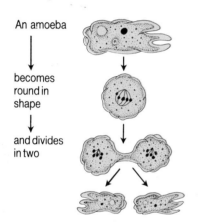

An amoeba

becomes round in shape

and divides in two

Amoeba takes about an hour to divide. The two parts separate to give two identical organisms.

Paramecium reproduces in the same way. Notice the fine hairs or cilia round both parts.

Hydras and sea anemones are made up of many cells. They reproduce asexually by growing buds. A bud starts off as a swelling. Then it develops tentacles, a mouth and a gut, and splits off the parent.

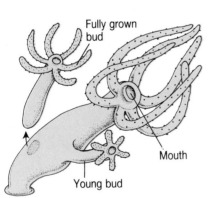

Fully grown bud

Mouth

Young bud

An adult Hydra. The bud on the right has grown its tentacles and is ready to break off.

After separating, the new bud floats away, settles down to feed and grows into an adult.

The beadlet sea anemone grows pink buds inside its body, then squirts them out of its mouth.

Sexual reproduction

In sexual reproduction there are two parents. The parents have **sex organs** which produce **sex cells**. In animals the male sex cells are called **sperms**. Sperms are produced by sex organs called **testes**. Female sex cells are called **eggs** or **ova** (one is an ovum). Ova are produced by sex organs called **ovaries**.

Here is an example of sexual reproduction.

Female sticklebacks produce eggs.

Male sticklebacks produce sperms.

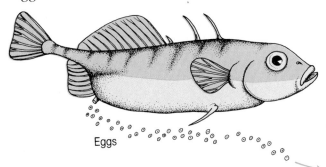

Eggs

Sperms

A sperm enters an egg. This is called **fertilization**.

A fertilized egg divides many times to form a ball of cells. The cells develop into a baby stickleback. A partly-formed baby is called an **embryo**.

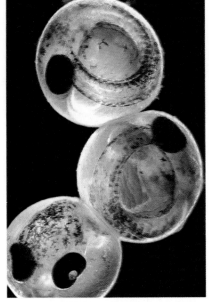

These stickleback embryos are nine days old.

External and internal fertilization

A female stickleback's eggs are fertilized outside her body. This is an example of **external fertilization**.

In insects, reptiles, birds, and mammals (including humans) the male puts his sperm into the female's body. So the eggs are fertilized inside her. This is called **internal fertilization**.

Plants reproduce sexually. You can read about them on page 52.

Questions

1   How is sexual reproduction different from asexual reproduction?

2   **a)** What are male sex cells and female sex cells called?

b) Name the organ which produces male sex cells.

c) Name the organ which produces female sex cells.

8·2 Human reproduction I

Sexual development in boys

Sometime between 11 and 16, a boy goes through these changes:
1 his voice becomes deeper
2 hair starts to grow on his face and body
3 his muscles develop
4 his testes start producing **sperm**.

These changes are caused by a hormone called **testosterone** produced by the boy's testes.

The changes that take place in young people during sexual development are called puberty.

Male sex organs

Male sex organs make male sex cells called **sperms**. They pass them into a woman's body during sexual intercourse.

A **testis** makes sperms and the male hormone testosterone. A man has two testes.

The **penis** passes sperms from the man's body into the woman's body during sexual intercourse.

These spaces are called **erectile tissue**. Before intercourse they fill with blood, making the penis stiff and erect.

Anus

These **sperm tubes** carry sperms from the testes to the penis. Sperms are carried in a liquid called **semen**.

These **glands** make the liquid part of semen. It contains chemicals which cause the sperms to swim after they enter the woman's body.

Sexual development in girls

Sometime between 8 and 15, a girl goes through these changes:
1 her breasts get bigger
2 her hips get more rounded
3 hair starts to grow on parts of her body
4 her ovaries start releasing eggs (ova).

These changes are caused by a hormone called **oestrogen** produced by the girl's ovaries.

Girls develop sexually earlier than boys do. But of course it varies from person to person.

Female sex organs

Female sex organs make ova, and protect and feed an ovum if it is fertilized and develops into a baby.

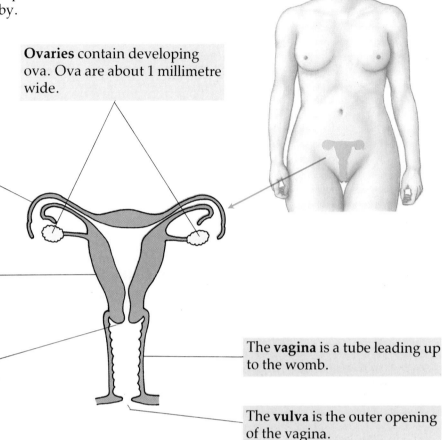

Ovaries contain developing ova. Ova are about 1 millimetre wide.

Fallopian tubes have funnel-shaped openings which catch ova as they come out of the ovaries. Ova move down these tubes to the womb.

The **womb** or **uterus** is a bag in which a fertilized ovum develops into a baby.

The **cervix** is a ring of muscle which closes the lower end of the womb.

The **vagina** is a tube leading up to the womb.

The **vulva** is the outer opening of the vagina.

Sexual intercourse

During sexual intercourse the man's penis becomes stiff and erect. He moves it backwards and forwards inside the woman's vagina. This causes semen to pump from his testes, through his penis, into the woman's body.

Questions

1 Which part of the body:
   a) produces sperms?
   b) produces ova?
   c) passes sperms from a man to a woman?
2 Name the liquid that contains sperms.
3 How does oestrogen affect a girl's body?

4 How does testosterone affect a boy's body?
5 What are female sex cells called?
6 How do sperms get into a woman's body to fertilize an ovum?
7 Where does a fertilized ovum develop into a baby?

Human reproduction II

The start of a new life

Human reproduction begins with sexual intercourse. During sexual intercourse millions of sperms pass from a man's penis into a woman's vagina. One of them may fertilize an ovum. This diagram shows how it all happens.

Sperms clustering round an ovum. Only one sperm will succeed in getting through the wall of the egg, to fertilize it.

2 The bubble bursts squirting its ovum out of the ovary. This is called **ovulation**. The ovum is sucked into a Fallopian tube.

3 Sperms in the Fallopian tube are attracted to the ovum. One sperm burrows into the ovum. The sperm nucleus and the ovum nucleus join. This is called **fertilization**. A skin forms round the ovum to keep out the other sperms.

Ovary

Lining of the womb

1 **Ova** develop inside bubbles in an ovary. A bubble grows until it bulges from the ovary.

4 The fertilized ovum divides to make a ball of about a hundred cells. This is called an **embryo**. The embryo moves down the Fallopian tube to the womb.

5 The embryo sinks into the thick lining of the womb. This is called **implantation**. The embryo gets food and oxygen from the blood vessels in the lining of the womb. This allows it to grow into a baby.

If an ovum is *not* fertilized after ovulation, it dies. But another ovum is released about a month later, as part of the **menstrual cycle**.

The menstrual cycle

Every month changes take place in a woman's body. These changes are called the **menstrual cycle**, or **monthly period**. They usually begin when a girl is between 8 and 15 years old.

2 During the week after ovulation the womb grows a thick lining of glands and blood vessels. The womb is now ready to protect and feed a fertilized ovum.

1 Ovulation produces a new ovum about every 28 days. The ovum is sucked into a Fallopian tube. If the woman has sexual intercourse the ovum may be fertilized. The woman is then **pregnant**. But if the ovum is not fertilized it dies within a few days.

3 About 14 days after ovulation, if the woman is not pregnant, the thick lining of the womb breaks down. Blood and dead cells flow out of her vagina. This is called **menstruation**, or a **period**. Then the cycle starts again.

When a woman is between 45 and 55 years old, her periods stop. This change is called the **menopause**, or **change of life**.

Questions

1 What is ovulation? How often does it happen?

2 Where in the body does an ovum get fertilized?

3 How do sperms reach the ovum?

4 How does a fertilized ovum become an embryo?

5 Explain what implantation means.

6 During the menstrual cycle:
   a) why does the womb grow a thick lining?
   b) what happens when this lining breaks down?

8·4 Life before birth

A baby feeds, breathes, and gets rid of waste inside a mother's body. The mother's blood brings it food and oxygen and carries the wastes away. But the mother's blood does not mix with the baby's blood. Food, oxygen, and wastes are exchanged in the **placenta**.

The placenta is shaped like a pancake, and is attached to the wall of the womb. There are blood vessels and spaces inside it. The baby's blood flows into the blood vessels. The mother's blood flows into the spaces. Substances are exchanged through the baby's blood vessel walls.

It is important for a pregnant woman to eat healthy food, to give the baby a good start in life.

1 The baby's blood carries carbon dioxide and other wastes to the placenta, along an **artery** in the **umbilical cord**.

2 The mother's blood flows into the spaces in the **placenta**, carrying food and oxygen.

3 The food and oxygen pass into the baby's blood through the thin walls of the blood vessels. At the same time the **wastes** pass out of the baby's blood.

4 The mother's blood carries the wastes away.

5 The baby's blood carries food and oxygen back to the baby along a **vein** in the **umbilical cord**.

The baby is in a bag of liquid called the **amnion**. This cushions it against knocks and bumps as the mother moves about.

How the baby develops

A fertilized ovum is smaller than a full-stop. In nine months, it will have grown into a baby weighing around three kilograms, and measuring about half a metre.

At 4–5 weeks

The embryo is about half a centimetre long. It has a bulge which will be its head, containing a developing brain, eyes, and ears. It has a tail, and lumps which will turn into arms and legs. A small heart pumps blood along an umbilical cord to the placenta.

At 8–10 weeks

It is now 4 centimetres long. It has a face, and limbs with fingers and toes. Most of its organs are fully developed. From now until birth it is called a **foetus**.

At 16 weeks

It is about 16 centimetres long. It is turning into a boy or a girl. The mother will soon feel it moving inside her.

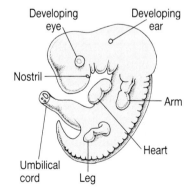

Use the drawing on the right to name the parts of the baby in each photograph.

Questions

1 How does a baby get food inside the womb?
2 How does a baby get oxygen inside the womb?
3 How does a baby get rid of its wastes while inside the womb?
4 Think of a reason why the mother's blood is not allowed to mix with the baby's blood.
5 The umbilical cord has two tubes inside it. What are these tubes? What do they do?
6 What is the amnion? How does it help the baby?
7 What is a foetus?

Birth, and birth control

During pregnancy, the wall of the womb develops thick, strong muscles ready for the baby's birth.

Birth begins with **labour**. The womb muscles start to contract. After some time the contractions push the baby head-first out of the womb.

At first the womb muscles contract about every half hour. Then the contractions get faster and stronger. They push the baby's head through the cervix into the vagina.

The contractions become very strong. The baby moves to a face-down position and is pushed out of the mother's body. It breathes air for the first time.

A few minutes later more contractions push the placenta and umbilical cord out of the womb. These are called the **after-birth**.

Placenta

Umbilical cord

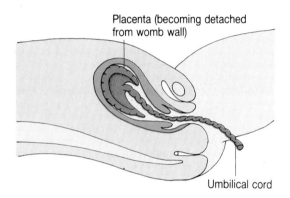

Placenta (becoming detached from womb wall)

Umbilical cord

Health of the mother

When a women is pregnant, she must take care of her health.

German measles (rubella). If a mother gets rubella during the first 12 weeks of pregnancy the germs can damage her baby, causing deafness, blindness, and heart disease. Pregnant women should avoid people who have rubella. Young girls should be innoculated against the disease.

Alcohol. If a pregnant woman drinks alcohol, it can slow her baby's development, damage its brain, and cause it to be born early.

Smoking. Pregnant women who smoke have smaller babies than non-smokers. Their babies are more likely to be born dead.

Health of the baby

When the baby is born it is put on the mother's breast or stomach immediately. This helps love develop between mother and child. Mother's milk is the perfect food for babies. It is free, always ready, and pure. Mother's milk protects babies from germs. If a mother is unable to breast feed, special powdered cow's milk may be used.

Another successful birth. The scissors is for cutting the umbilical cord.

Birth control

Birth control, or **contraception**, lets couples decide how many children they want. These are some of the methods used.

The condom. The **condom** or sheath is a thin rubber cover for the penis. It is put on before intercourse. Sperms get trapped inside it.

Condoms are quite reliable. But they are even safer if the woman uses a **spermicide**. This is a chemical which kills sperms. The woman puts a spermicide cream or jelly into her vagina before intercourse.

The diaphragm. The **diaphragm** is a circle of rubber with a metal spring round it. Before intercourse, the woman smears it with spermicide. Then she puts it into her vagina, to cover the cervix. It stops sperms getting into the womb. For safety, it is left in place for at least eight hours.

Contraceptive pills. Contraceptive pills contain female hormones. They do three things:

1 they prevent the ovaries from releasing ova

2 they stop an ovum moving along a Fallopian tube

3 they fill the entrance to the womb with a sticky substance so that sperms cannot swim through.

Contraceptive pills are very reliable. But they should not be used by women with liver disease or diabetes. Also some doctors think that women who smoke may develop blood clots, migraine headaches, or heart conditions, if they take the Pill. Some may also develop breast cancer.

The rhythm method. Some people feel it is wrong to use any kind of birth control except the **rhythm method**. In this method the couple avoids sexual intercourse when there is an ovum ready to be fertilized. Knowing when the ovum can be fertilized is difficult to work out. This method is not very reliable.

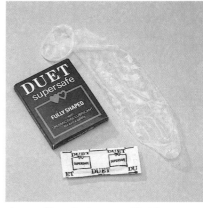

As well as being a reliable contraceptive, condoms also protect against infection.

Some women choose the diaphragm or cap as a contraceptive.

It is essential to talk to the doctor before using the Pill. It can damage the health of some women.

Questions

1 What causes a baby to be pushed out of the womb?

2 Which part of the baby normally comes out first?

3 What is the after-birth?

4 Why should young girls be innoculated against rubella?

5 Why should pregnant women avoid alcohol and smoking?

6 How does a condom prevent pregnancy?

7 What is a spermicide? Which methods of contraception are made safer by spermicides?

8 Which women might find contraceptive pills harmful?

8·6 Population

Every day, the number of people in the world increases by 200 000. So every second there are two more mouths to feed.

The population explosion means that the world is getting crowded. Although the Earth has enough resources for us all, still millions starve. We must take action.

Why the world's population is increasing

The world's population is increasing because:

1 better medicines and health care are helping us to fight disease

2 clean water supplies and better sewage disposal mean that diseases do not spread so easily

3 modern farming methods have given some countries more food

This means fewer babies die, and adults live longer than they used to. But in poor countries millions of people starve to death each year. Population growth is only one reason why.

Why do millions starve?

Right now there is enough food in the world for everyone. So why do millions of people starve?

1 Unequal sharing. People in rich countries build up huge stores of food, and eat far more than they need. The average European gets through enough food and other materials for 40 poor Africans.

This drawing shows the amount of food eaten in rich and poor countries each year.

= 25 kg of food

Hunger line
250 kg of food should be eaten each year to stay healthy.

2 Growing the wrong crops. Poor countries often use their best land for tobacco, tea, coffee, and other crops they can sell to rich countries, instead of growing food for their own people.

3 Creating deserts. Tropical forests are cut down to make room for more crops. But fewer trees mean less rain. The soil is baked hard by the sun and turns into desert.

4 Population growth. People in the poorer countries tend to have the largest families. So every year it becomes more difficult for poor countries to feed, clothe, and educate everyone.

A tropical forest being cut down in Brazil, to make way for crops and cattle ranches. The exposed topsoil will soon get worn away by wind and rain.

Land is used to grow crops like coffee for sale instead of for feeding the local people.

Action needed

1 The best farm land should be used to grow food to feed the local population and tropical forests should be looked after to stop the spread of deserts.

2 It is very important to stop the growth in population. This is difficult to do, because poor families feel they need many children to help farm the land, earn money, and make them happy. Better education and health is needed for all, as well as advice on birth control.

3 Rich countries must help, but not just with food and money. They can help improve education, irrigation, and farming methods in poorer countries.

Questions

1 Use the graph on the opposite page to find out:
   a) the population of the world now
   b) the population in the year 2000, if it keeps growing at its present rate.

2 World population rose rapidly after the year 1800. Suggest some reasons for this.

3 The population is growing faster in poor countries than in rich ones. Why is this?

4 Why do some countries use their best land for crops like tobacco and coffee, rather than food?

5 Clearing tropical forests to grow crops can make things worse in the long run. Explain why.

8·A Embryos, babies and abortion

Abortion

Anything which ends a pregnancy before 28 weeks is called an **abortion**. Up to this time a baby has not developed enough to survive outside its mother. Abortions can occur naturally (spontaneously), or they can be done deliberately (be induced) for various reasons.

Spontaneous abortion (miscarriage). As many as 30 per cent of fertilized ova fail to develop into babies. The embryo dies and is expelled from the womb but many are so tiny and undeveloped that the miscarriage goes unnoticed, or may be confused with a normal period (menstruation). Some embryos fail to become attached to the uterus wall (implantation) and about half that do are aborted spontaneously, usually because the ovum is defective or because the embryo or placenta is developing abnormally.

1 Some people think that induced abortion should not be allowed because it is the deliberate destruction of a human life.

2 When does life begin: when an ovum is fertilized; at the stage of development when a baby is just able to survive on its own, or at the moment of normal birth?

3 Think about these issues, and discuss them with friends, parents and teachers.

Induced abortion. A pregnancy can be deliberately ended if the health of the mother is in serious danger, if there is a risk of the child being born with serious handicap or if the mother feels that she will be unable to care for the child. The operation must be approved by two doctors, and the earlier it is done the better. It is safest before week 13 of development, when the foetus can be sucked from the uterus through a tube. Removal at a later stage may involve a surgical operation, or the use of chemicals which cause labour to begin early and push the baby out of the uterus.

Embryo research

Human embryos can be obtained by putting ova, sucked from a woman's ovaries with a special syringe, in a container with sperms and keeping them warm for about 60 hours. Sperms fertilize the ova, which develop into embryos (see photograph and diagram). This technique is used for several purposes:

Test tube babies. Embryos produced in this way can be placed in the wombs of women who cannot have a baby by normal means. About 10 per cent implant and develop. More than a thousand babies have been produced this way so far.

Development of contraceptives. New contraceptives are being developed which prevent ova growing into babies. New products are tested by taking ova from women treated with a contraceptive and placing them in a container with sperms to see if they are fertilized and develop.

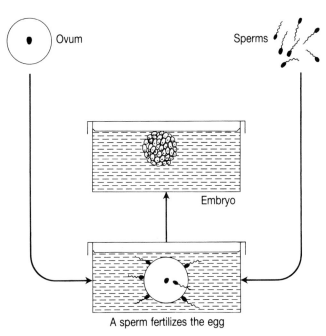

A sperm fertilizes the egg

158

Prevention of genetic diseases. By studying the detailed metabolism and development of early embryos it is hoped to find ways of identifying those which could develop genetic diseases such as Downs' syndrome (Unit 2.8) and muscular dystrophy. If this were possible defective embryos could be removed before they develop.

Do you think these techniques should be banned (are they unethical)? Read the following then write out arguments for and against them.

1 About a quarter of a million women in Britain are infertile.

2 There are 125 000 induced abortions in Britain each year. Would safer contraceptives reduce this figure?

3 About 7000 babies a year are born with genetic diseases.

4 Should only spontaneously aborted embryos be used for research? Can you think of arguments against this idea?

Lactation: the production of milk

During pregnancy the ovary and placenta produce hormones which cause milk-producing glands in the breasts to develop. After birth the pituitary gland (Unit 7.7) produces a hormone which starts milk production. A suckling baby sets off nerve impulses which cause the 'let-down' reflex, which starts milk flowing.

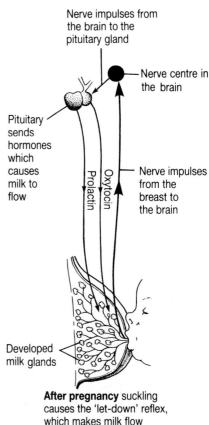

Nerve impulses from the brain to the pituitary gland

Nerve centre in the brain

Pituitary sends hormones which causes milk to flow

Prolactin Oxytocin

Nerve impulses from the breast to the brain

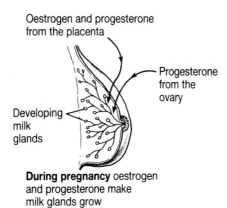

Oestrogen and progesterone from the placenta

Progesterone from the ovary

Developing milk glands

During pregnancy oestrogen and progesterone make milk glands grow

Developed milk glands

After pregnancy suckling causes the 'let-down' reflex, which makes milk flow

Use the information below to produce a chart showing the advantages and disadvantages of breast feeding and bottle feeding.

Suited to a baby's needs. Bottle milk is made from dried cow's milk adjusted by adding and taking away substances to make it similar to breast milk. The contents of breast milk exactly meet the needs of a growing baby.

Free from germs. The bottle and its teat, and the water used to dissolve the milk have to be carefully sterilized before use, then warmed to the right temperature. Breast milk is pure and fresh, always at the right temperature, and instantly available.

Expense. Bottle milk is expensive, and breast milk is free.

Digestion. Breast milk is more quickly digested than bottle milk. This is one reason why breast-fed babies rarely suffer from constipation, and so cry less.

Allergies. Breast-fed babies are less likely to have allergies such as sensitivity to pollen.

Immunity. Breast milk contains antibodies. These destroy many germs that threaten babies. It also contains phagocytes, white blood cells which destroy germs (unit 5.4). So breast-fed babies have less diarrhoea and skin disorders like nappy rash.

Development. Breast milk contains large amounts of taurine, a substance which is important for the development of the nervous system. There is very little taurine in bottle milk.

Feeding. Anyone can bottle feed a baby. Breast milk can be expressed into a bottle if necessary. During breast feeding the close body contact between mother and baby is especially warm and loving. The let-down reflex can be very pleasant for the mother. A few women are unable to breast feed their baby. Some do not breast feed because they feel it is less convenient.

8·B Problems of population growth

During the time it takes you to read this sentence four people, most of them children, will have died of starvation somewhere in the world. This is happening because some countries too poor to import food have more people than the land, as it is managed at the moment, can support. The problem is getting worse because of population growth. Find out more about population growth from the table below.

1 Put these areas in order from the fastest to the slowest population growth rates.
2 Now sort them into rich and poor (or developed and developing) areas. Do rich or poor areas have the fastest population growth?
3 Think of reasons for what you have discovered.
4 What do you think 'doubling time' means?

Area	Pop. 1985	Birth Rate	Death Rate	% incr. pa	Doubling Time	Pop. 2000
Africa	551m	45	16	+ 2.9	24 yrs	869m
Asia	2829m	28	10	+ 1.8	39 yrs	3562m
Europe	492m	13	10	+ 0.3	240 yrs	509m
Latin America	406m	31	8	+ 2.3	30 yrs	554m
North America	264m	15	8	+ 0.7	99 yrs	297m
World	4845m	27	11	+ 1.7	41 yrs	6135m

Population growth in rich (developed) areas

Population increase in rich nations is slowing down, and in some it may soon stop. The main reason is that increased mechanization means that fewer people are needed to produce food, so large families are no longer needed for survival. Another reason for smaller families should be clear after reading the text opposite.

The cost of having children is increasing. In the USA it can cost $100 000 to support a child to 18 years of age, excluding education fees.

Population growth in poor (developing) countries

Work out for yourself why poor countries tend to have large families.

1 In many poor areas children are working to support the family by at least 10 years of age.

2 Also, a couple in some poor areas has to produce 10 children to be 95 per cent certain of having a son who will survive to 40 years of age.

Reasons for having children	Birth rate	Economic support	Love etc.	Other
Mexico	High	72%	16%	12%
Singa-pore	Med.	19%	65%	16%
USA	Low	4%	73%	23%

Source: East-West Population Institute

	Infant Mortality Rate*	Birth Rate**
Rich countries	15	16
Middle-income countries	25	31
Poor countries	129	41

*Deaths per 1,000 live births
**Births per 1,000 people per year
Source: UNFPA

Doubling time

Large families compensate for high child death rates and children help support the family from an early age. But think what it means for a poor country's population to double in 25 years.
1 Just to keep today's poor standard of nutrition, food supplies must be doubled so more wild habitats will be destroyed. Damage from over-grazing and pollution by excess pesticides and fertilizers will increase.

2 Electricity and water supplies, sewage disposal and refuse collection systems will have to be doubled. What other problems are there?

These would be near impossible tasks in a rich area. Poor areas will have their resources stretched to the limit, and living conditions will inevitably decline. Unit 8.6 outlines possible solutions and here are some more.

Crops versus animals

Meat and dairy produce brings a higher price than plant crops, so farmers in poor countries try to pack as many animals as possible on to pasture, rather than grow crops. There is a danger that all vegetation will be eaten away and soil compacted by animal hooves. Then rain no longer soaks into the ground but rushes over the surface stripping away soil. In fine weather the land, unprotected by vegetation, is baked hard by the sun, so pasture is turned into desert. Read the information opposite and think about some solutions.

Avoidable waste of food

Up to 50 per cent of food is wasted between the field and the consumer. Poor harvesting causes grains to be spilled and broken open and fruit to be bruised. Damp food goes mouldy during storage, and badly stored food can be ruined by insects and rats. Solving these problems would be expensive, but is it worthwhile?

1 It takes 30 times more land to produce 1 kg of animal protein as it does to produce the same amount of plant protein.
2 The leaves of crop plants, at present thrown away, can be used to make cheap animal food.
*3 Soya flour, and other cheap plant foods can be converted into **textured vegetable protein** – a substitute for meat.*
What have these facts got to do with the animal versus crop controversy?

Hippopotamus

Food from wild animals

1 Africa has up to 30 wild, hoofed animals which, after millions of years of evolution, can feed off wild plants and resist tropical diseases. Their meat can be as good if not better than those from domesticated animals.

2 Cattle, sheep and goats can only live on pasture, and cannot resist tropical diseases. Think of arguments for and against clearing away wild habitats for pasture?

In Africa the hippopotamus and eland are already sources of meat. The oryx is one of the few meat producing species which can live in deserts. In Europe the red deer can live on moss and grass too poor for other animals and there are schemes to 'farm' bison, capybara and vicuña in the USA.

Oryx

If carefully managed, wildlife can provide a stable, pollution-free source of food and materials which is endless. It will also attract a lucrative tourist trade.

A problem is the expense of finding and killing animals of the right age, size, condition and sex in vast areas of wilderness often impassable to motor vehicles. One solution is to develop large 'farms' or 'ranches' where animals can wander freely in conditions which are as near natural as possible.

Eland

Questions

1 *Recall knowledge*
Copy the following sentences and fill in the gaps.
   a) In . . . . . reproduction there is only one parent.
   b) *Amoeba* reproduces asexually by . . . . .
   c) Male sex cells of animals are called . . . . .
   d) They are produced by organs called . . . . .
   e) Female sex cells of animals are called . . . . .
   f) They are produced by organs called . . . . .
   g) . . . . . is the joining together of a male sex cell and a female sex cell.
   h) A fertilized cell is called a . . . . . It develops into a baby.
   i) A partly-developed baby is called an . . . . .

2 *Recall knowledge*
   a) Name some animals that have external fertilization.
   b) Name some animals that have internal fertilization.
   c) Write down four advantages of having a baby develop inside its mother's body.
   d) Write down four disadvantages of having a baby develop outside its mother's body.

3 *Recall knowledge*
   a) How many sperms are needed to fertilize an ovum?
   b) What happens to the nucleus of a sperm and ovum during fertilization?
   c) Why does a skin form around an ovum immediately after fertilization?
   d) How long does it take for a fertilized human ovum to develop into a baby?
   e) Where does the implantation of an embryo take place?
   f) What does implantation mean?

4 *Recall knowledge*
   a) What is the scientific name for German measles?
   b) Describe two ways in which German measles can damage a developing baby.
   c) How can girls avoid catching this disease?
   d) Give three reasons why breast-feeding is better for babies than bottle-feeding?

5 *Recall knowledge*
Below is a diagram of a woman's reproductive system.
   a) Name the parts labelled B to G.
   b) Now match each of these descriptions to one of the labels:
      where fertilization occurs;
      the space where a baby develops;
      ovulation occurs in this organ;
      the lining of this part is shed once a month;
      a baby passes through these parts during delivery.
   c) Write down another name for a woman's period.
   d) What happens to the lining of the womb just after ovulation? Why does this change happen?

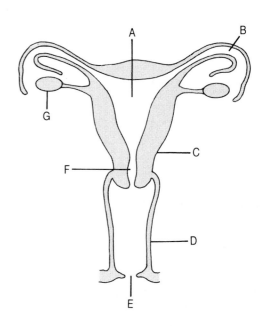

6 *Recall knowledge*
   a) What is a condom?
   b) What is a diaphragm?
   c) Why should a woman put spermicide inside her vagina before sexual intercourse when using a diaphragm or condom?
   d) What do contraceptive pills contain?
   e) Describe three ways in which contraceptive pills can prevent pregnancy.

7 *Recall knowledge*

Opposite is a man's reproductive system.
- **a)** Name the parts labelled A, B, C, D and E.
- **b)** Match each of these descriptions to one of the labels:

    passes sperms into the woman's reproductive organs during sexual intercourse;
    produces the hormone testosterone;
    makes the penis erect during intercourse;
    carry sperms from the testes to the penis;
    makes the liquid part of semen.
- **c)** List the changes which the hormone testosterone produces in boys. At about what age do these changes begin?
- **d)** List the changes which the hormone oestrogen produces in girls. At about what age do these changes begin?

8 *Recall knowledge*

The drawing opposite shows a developing baby inside the womb.
- **a)** Name the parts labelled A to D.
- **b)** What does part C contain?
- **c)** Name two substances which pass into the baby's blood from the mother's blood.
- **d)** Name one substance which passes from the baby's blood into the mother's blood.
- **e)** Where on the diagram do these substances pass between mother and baby?
- **f)** What does part B do during birth?
- **g)** A few minutes after a baby is born the after-birth is pushed out of the womb. Name the parts of the after-birth. Which letters on the diagram point to these parts?

9 *Recall knowledge/interpret data*
- **a)** From the graph opposite, find out: the population of the world in 1900 and its population in 1970.
- **b)** Describe how the population changed between those two years.
- **c)** Write down as many reasons as you can to explain this change.
- **d)** What problems has the growth in world population caused?
- **e)** Give three reasons why millions of people are starving to death when there is enough food for everyone in the world?
- **f)** Write down two actions that rich countries can take to help poor countries.

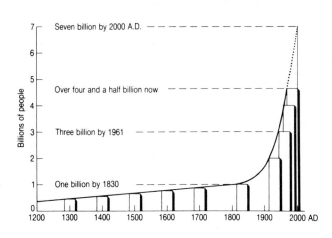

9.1 Depending on each other

Producers and consumers

All living things need energy. They get their energy from food. Plants are called **producers** because they make their own food. They use sunlight to make food by photosynthesis.

Without plants, humans and all other animals would starve to death. This is because they *cannot* make their own food. The only way animals can obtain energy is by eating, or consuming, plants or other animals. So animals are called **consumers**.

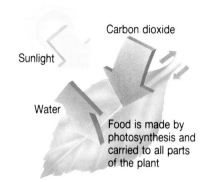

Sunlight

Carbon dioxide

Water

Food is made by photosynthesis and carried to all parts of the plant

Food chains

Eaten by

Eaten by

1 Seaweed is a **producer**. It produces food by photosynthesis.

2 Periwinkles are called **first consumers** because they eat seaweed.

3 Herring gulls are called **second consumers**, because they eat periwinkles.

Seaweed ⟶ periwinkle ⟶ herring gull.

This is an example of a food chain.

Food chains show how one living thing is the food for another. Energy passes along a food chain from producers to consumers as one member of the chain eats the next.

Food pyramids

On the right is a **food pyramid**. It shows how consumers can get larger in size, but smaller in number, as you go along the food chain.

When a moth caterpillar eats a leaf it uses up some of the energy from the leaf for itself. So there is less to pass on to a robin. That means the robin needs to eat several moth caterpillars to get enough energy. So there are fewer robins than caterpillars.

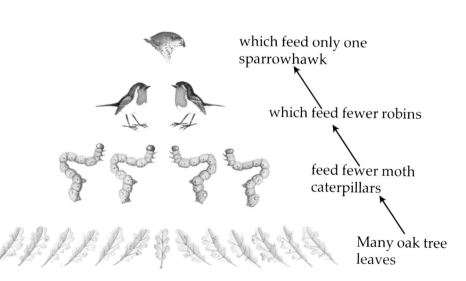

which feed only one sparrowhawk

which feed fewer robins

feed fewer moth caterpillars

Many oak tree leaves

Food webs

A plant or animal usually belongs to several food chains. For example, seaweeds are eaten by limpets and winkles as well as by sea worms. In this way food chains are connected together to make **food webs**. This diagram shows a food web in the sea.

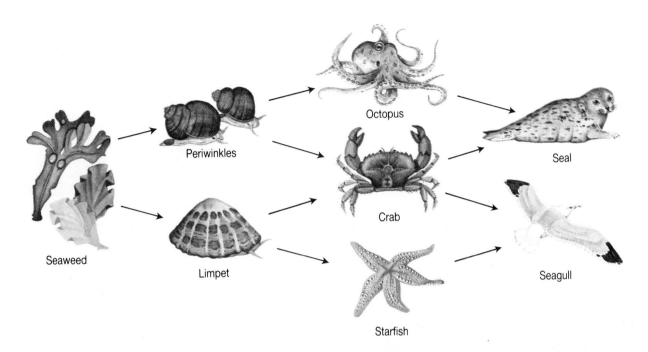

Octopus

Periwinkles

Seal

Crab

Seaweed

Limpet

Starfish

Seagull

Decomposers

Many fungi and bacteria are **decomposers**. They feed on dead animals and plants. First they produce digestive juices which make the dead things rot, or **decompose** into liquid. Then they absorb the liquid.

Decomposers are important because:
1 they get rid of dead animals and plants
2 they release chemicals from dead things which soak into the soil and help to keep it fertile

Fungi feeding on a dead tree. They turn the wood into liquid.

This apple is providing a feast for millions of bacteria.

Questions

1 Why are plants called producers?
2 Put this food chain in the correct order:
slug → fox → primrose leaf → frog
3 Explain how decomposers keep soil fertile.

4 In the food web above list:
a) the producers
b) the second consumers.
5 Now write down two food chains ending in seals.

9·2 The carbon cycle

All living things need carbon. It is needed for the proteins, fats, and other substances that make up living things. The carbon comes from carbon dioxide in the air.

Plants take in carbon dioxide from the air. They use it to make food by photosynthesis. Animals then get carbon by eating plants.

The amount of carbon dioxide in the air always stays the same, because it is returned to the air as fast as plants take it in.

1 Plants and animals give out carbon dioxide when they respire.

2 Bacteria and fungi respire and give out carbon dioxide while they are decomposing the bodies of dead animals and plants.

3 Wood, coal, gas, and petrol contain carbon. When they are burned the carbon combines with oxygen to form carbon dioxide. It goes off into the air.

Wood, coal, gas and oil started off as carbon dioxide. The gas is released again when they are burned.

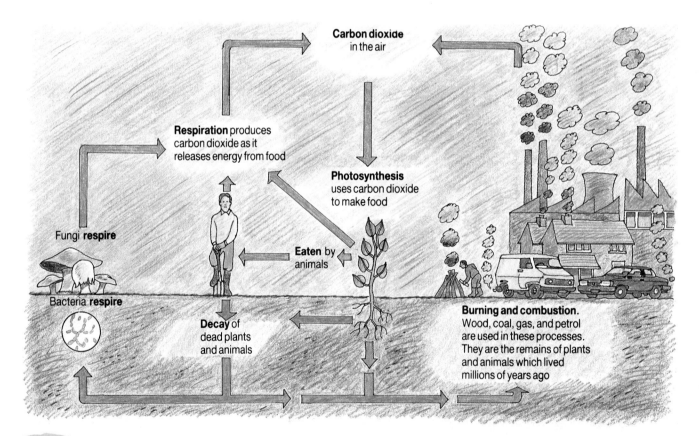

Carbon dioxide in the air

Respiration produces carbon dioxide as it releases energy from food

Photosynthesis uses carbon dioxide to make food

Fungi **respire**

Eaten by animals

Bacteria **respire**

Decay of dead plants and animals

Burning and combustion. Wood, coal, gas, and petrol are used in these processes. They are the remains of plants and animals which lived millions of years ago

Questions

1 How does carbon get from the air into the bodies of plants and animals?

2 Explain why the amount of carbon dioxide in the air stays the same.

166

9.3 The nitrogen cycle

All living things need nitrogen to make proteins. Air is four-fifths nitrogen. But neither plants nor animals can take it in from the air. First it has to be changed into **nitrates**.

Then plants obtain nitrogen by taking in nitrates from soil. Animals obtain nitrogen by eating plants, or other animals.

How nitrogen is turned into nitrates

1 **Lightning** makes air so hot that nitrogen and oxygen combine. They make chemicals which are washed into the soil, where they form nitrates.
2 **Nitrogen-fixing bacteria** live in soil, and in lumps called **root nodules** on the roots of clover, peas, and beans. They use nitrogen from the air to make nitrates, which are released into the plants or the soil.
3 **Nitrifying bacteria** make nitrates from animal droppings, and from the bodies of dead animals and plants.

Some soil nitrates are changed back into nitrogen by **denitrifying bacteria**. These live in the waterlogged soil of ponds and marshes.

Root nodules on a pea plant, homes for nitrogen-fixing bacteria. Because the bacteria feed them with nitrates, peas grow well even in poor soil.

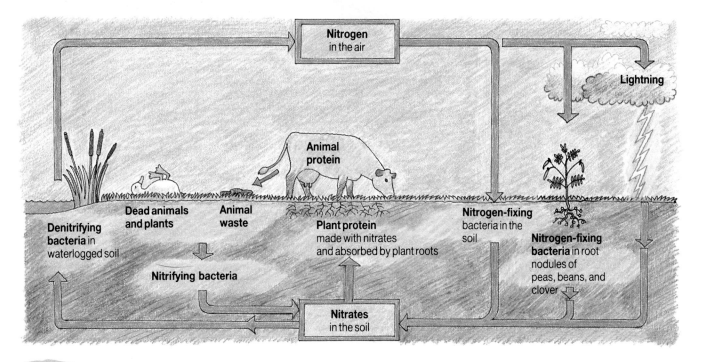

Questions

1 Why do living things need nitrogen?
2 How do plants obtain nitrogen?
3 How do animals obtain nitrogen?

4 Describe three ways in which nitrogen is changed into nitrates.
5 How are nitrates changed back into nitrogen?

9·4 Soil

All life on land depends on soil. Land plants need it for support, water, and minerals. Land animals need it because they eat plants, or other animals which eat plants.

Soil is made from small bits of **rock**, and from **humus** which is the decayed remains of dead animals and plants. The rock is broken into pieces by the weather. This is called **weathering**.

How soil is formed by weathering

1 Rock gets broken up when **rain water** soaks into it and freezes. Rain also contains weak acid which can dissolve rock and carry it away.

2 **Heat and cold** make rocks expand and contract. After a time this can make them crack.

First, weathering splits the rock into small pieces.

Then weathering breaks these down into smaller rock particles. Soil is formed when they mix with humus.

Some rock particles are washed into rivers and worn down ito sand, clay, and silt.

What soil is made of

If you shake up soil with water it settles into different layers.

Humus floats to the top. It is important because:

1 it is rich in minerals

2 it contains nitrogen-fixing bacteria

3 it sticks rock particles together so they don't get blown or washed away

4 it keeps soil moist because it soaks up water like a sponge.

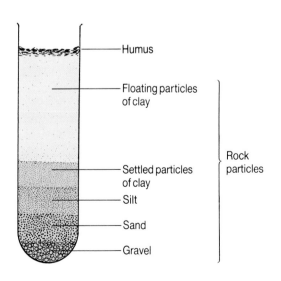

- Humus
- Floating particles of clay
- Settled particles of clay
- Silt
- Sand
- Gravel
- Rock particles

Fertile soil

The most fertile soil is called **loam**. Its rock particles are stuck together by humus into clumps called **soil crumbs**.

Soil crumbs stop minerals being washed from soil. They soak up water, and have air spaces in between them. So roots have minerals, moisture, and air. Soil crumbs also make soil easy to dig.

Soil crumbs

Air spaces

Water around the soil crumbs

Topsoil is very fertile. Humus gives it a dark colour. It is rich in minerals, and contains many living things.

Subsoil is lighter in colour because it has no humus. It is rich in minerals but has few living things, except plant roots.

Broken rocks

Solid rock

Fertilizers

Garden and farm soil must have fertilizers added, to replace the important minerals that plants use up.

Organic fertilizers include manure, well-rotted compost, dried blood, and bonemeal. These add humus as well as minerals to soil. But they work slowly because they must decompose first.

Inorganic fertilizers are chemicals made in factories. They dissolve in soil water, so plants can use them immediately. But if they are used over a long time, they harm soil by destroying soil crumbs.

Soil life

The most important living things in soil are the bacteria and earthworms. They both help to keep soil fertile. The bacteria decompose dead plants and animals. When the earthworms burrow through soil, they mix its layers together, and help air and water get into it. They also drag in leaves which rot to form humus.

An earthworm in its burrow. Earthworms eat the soil as they burrow through it. They digest some, and pass the rest out as worm casts.

Questions

1 How does weathering turn solid rock into soil?
2 What is humus?
3 Why is humus an important part of soil?

4 How can chemical fertilizers make soil less fertile?
5 How do earthworms help keep soil fertile?

9.5 The water cycle

Water is always on the move. It rises from seas, rivers, and lakes to the clouds and falls back again as rain. This is called the **water cycle.** Land plants and animals would die without the water cycle, and soil would turn to dust.

How the water cycle works

1 The sun warms seas, rivers, and lakes. The heat causes water to evaporate and turn into **water vapour**.
2 Plants and animals also give out water vapour.
3 As the water vapour rises it cools down and forms tiny water droplets. These gather as **clouds**.
4 When clouds cool down the water droplets join to form bigger and bigger drops. When the drops are heavy enough they fall as **rain**.
5 Streams and rivers take water back to the sea. Some water is taken up by plants and animals. The cycle starts again.

Questions

1 Why is the water cycle important?
2 What part does the sun play in the water cycle?

3 How are clouds and rain formed?
4 How does water get back to the sea?

9·6 Water pollution

Thousands of different plants and animals live in water. Water life can be killed and our water supplies poisoned if harmful substances, called **pollutants**, get into the water.

Some water pollutants

Waste from factories may contain poisonous chemicals such as cyanide, mercury, or lead. These can pass along food chains to fish. So birds, humans, and other fish-eating animals get poisoned.

Fertilizers sprayed onto fields can soak into rivers and lakes where they cause algae to grow fast. The algae spread over the surface blocking out light from the plants below. The plants die and are decomposed by bacteria which use up all the oxygen. So fish and all other water life die too.

Pesticides are sprayed onto crops to kill insects and other pests. But they also kill wildlife in hedgerows, ponds, and streams.

Waste from farms is called **slurry**. It is a mixture of animal droppings and urine. It is sprayed onto fields as fertilizer. Because it is liquid, it can easily seep through the ground into streams and rivers, and pollute them.

Oil spilled from tankers and offshore oil rigs poisons sea birds, and clogs their feathers so they cannot fly. It also kills animals and plants that live along the sea shore, and spoils holiday beaches.

The River Nishua in the USA: a dead river, polluted by waste from paper mills.

Pesticide kills harmful pests – and harmless wildlife too.

The water we drink is free from pollutants. We do not poison ourselves – yet!

A puffin killed by oil from a stricken tanker.

Questions

1 What is a pollutant? Name three pollutants.
2 How can fertilizers kill water life?

3 Describe two ways in which water pollution can harm humans.

9·7 More about pollution

Air pollution

Air is polluted by smoke, dust, and harmful gases. Most of these come from power stations, factories, cars, buses, and lorries.

Smoke contains tiny particles of carbon (soot). This blackens buildings. It covers plant leaves so that photosynthesis slows down. The smoke from car engines also contains lead, which can cause brain damage in young children.

Dust from quarries, saw mills, and asbestos factories can cause lung disease.

Harmful gases. The main ones are **sulphur dioxide** and **nitrogen oxides**. These form when coal, oil, and petrol are burned in power stations, factories, engines, and homes. They damage plant leaves, and aggravate diseases like bronchitis.

When sulphur dioxide and nitrogen oxides rise into the air they can dissolve in clouds and form acids. Then they fall back to earth as **acid rain**. This rain corrodes metal railings and bridges, and eats away stonework on buildings.

It's difficult for a leaf to photosynthesize when it's completely covered in soot!

Acid rain damage

Acid rain eats away stonework. This was once an angel.

Spruce trees in Germany, killed by acid rain.

Some pollution from cars...

...falls as acid rain.

172

Other kinds of pollution

Radiation. There is a risk that radiation will escape from nuclear power stations and from stored radioactive waste. Radiation can cause cancer and leukaemia.

Litter. Plastic bags and drink cans do not rot. Even paper takes a long time to rot. People who dump litter in the countryside are spoiling our beauty spots.

Noise. Noise from cars, motorcycles, aeroplanes, dogs, children, radios, and televisions can be a form of pollution. It can irritate people and cause mental depression. Prolonged loud noise from disco music and factory machinery can make people deaf.

If you live near an airport, you'll know all about noise pollution.

Some ways to cut down pollution

1 By passing laws. The Clean Air Act of 1968 is an example. It turned many places into smokeless zones, where you may burn only smokeless fuel.

2 Cleaner smoke and fumes. Cleaning systems can be fitted to power station chimneys and car exhaust pipes. They stop sulphur dioxide and other pollutants from escaping into the air.

3 Cleaner fuel. Coal and oil can be treated to remove sulphur before they are burned in power stations. Petrol companies are reducing the amount of lead in petrol.

We can help cut down pollution by buying leadfree petrol . . .

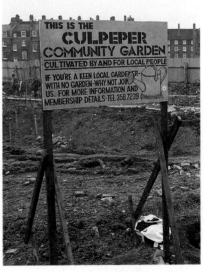

. . . and joining schemes to clear-up wasteland.

Questions

1 How can soot cause damage?
2 a) Name two harmful gases which pollute the air.
   b) Where do these gases come from?
3 a) How is acid rain formed?
   b) Describe the damage which acid rain can do.
4 a) Why is radiation dangerous?
   b) Where could harmful radiation come from?
5 Why must you always take litter home with you after visiting the countryside?
6 When does noise become a form of pollution?
7 Describe three ways of cutting down pollution.

9·8 Don't throw it away!

We live in a wasteful, throw-away world. We buy things in packaging which we tear off and throw away. Bottles and cans are used once and thrown away. Some things are deliberately made so they can't be mended, or to wear out quickly and be thrown away. But nearly three quarters of what we throw away *could* be used again!

Re-use

Millions of metal, glass and plastic containers are thrown away which could be used again. Old clothes can be sold, given away or used to make something else. Bits of old cars can be used to mend other cars. Think of other things we can re-use.

Recycling waste materials

Recycling means turning materials from old or broken things into new goods. Paper and card can be made into pulp and used to make recycled paper. Rags can be shredded and made into cheap cloth. Glass, metal and certain plastics can be melted down and used to make new goods.

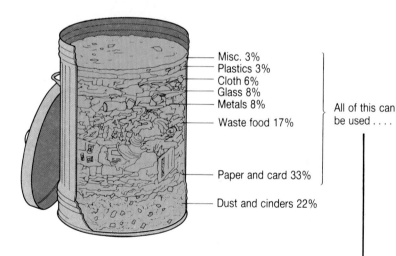

Misc. 3%
Plastics 3%
Cloth 6%
Glass 8%
Metals 8%
Waste food 17%
Paper and card 33%
Dust and cinders 22%

All of this can be used . . . .

To make these

Why recycling is important

1 Recycling means less land is needed for ugly, smelly rubbish tips, and it reduces the risk of pollution from rubbish tips.

2 Recycling slows the rate at which the Earth is ripped up for minerals and forests are cut down for wood and paper.

3 Recycling saves energy. When you throw away metal or glass you also throw away the energy used to make it. It takes far less energy to melt down scrap metal and use it again than to produce it from metal ore.

Clean, replaceable sources of energy

When a car engine burns a litre of petrol the petrol has gone forever and gases from the engine have polluted the air. But some sources of energy are clean, and can be easily replaced.

Alcohol. The sugar and starch in sugar cane, corn and potatoes can be fermented into a type of alcohol which can be used instead of petrol in cars.

Methane gas. We throw away the leaves of food plants when they could be placed in containers and allowed to rot. This produces methane gas which can be used for heating, cooking or making electricity. What is left of the plants makes animal food and fertilizer.

Solar power. Solar panels trap energy from the sun to heat water. This saves gas and electricity.

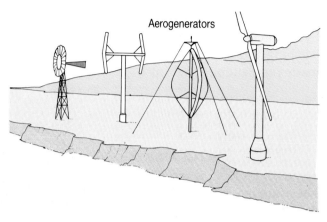

Wind power. In areas where strong steady winds blow windmills can be used to produce electricity.

Geothermal power. The deeper you go towards the centre of the earth the hotter it gets. Water can be pumped deep into the ground where it is changed to steam by hot rocks. The steam is piped to the surface to heat homes and work electricity generators.

Questions

1 What is the difference between re-using and recycling? List six ways *you* could re-use and recycle things.

2 Seventy per cent of metal is used once then thrown away. How does recycling it save metal and energy?

3 Can you think of any more clean, replaceable sources of energy?

Supplies of clean water

Every day you use about 160 litres of water, for drinking, cooking, washing and so on. Where does it all come from, and how is it made pure enough to drink?

Some comes from deep wells called **bore holes**, which take water from water-filled rocks, or **aquifers**.

Some comes from **reservoirs**. These are made by building a dam across a river valley so the valley fills with water.

Some is taken from rivers. This is called **river abstraction**.

Screening. Metal grids placed where water is taken from rivers and reservoirs keep out floating weeds and rubbish.

Sedimentation. The water is pumped into tanks where large particles settle to the bottom. They form a **sediment** which is piped away.

Coagulation. Chemicals are added to the water to make small bits of dirt stick together (coagulate) so they can be filtered out.

Chlorination. Then chlorine is added to kill germs.

Bore holes · Storage tank · Chlorine added · Pump · Rain · Impervious rock · Porous rock (aquifer) · Porous rock full of water · Alum added · Pressure filter · Reservoir · Rain · Pump · River abstraction · Pump · Screen (traps debris) · Storage tank · Consumer · Pump · Chlorine added · Filter bed · Coagulation tank · Sedimentation tank

Sewage disposal

Sewage consists of liquid and solid waste from our bodies (faeces and urine), water from washing and some industrial wastes. It contains harmful germs. It must be disposed of so that it does not get into drinking water. This is done in a sewage treatment works.

1 Screening. First wire nets strain out sticks, paper, rags and so on. These are burned or buried.

2 Grit tanks. The screened sewage is passed into large tanks where grit, stones and other heavy objects sink to the bottom.

Sludge used to make fertilizer and methane gas

4 Aeration tank

Air   Air   Air

2 Grit tank

Untreated sewage

1 Screening

3 Sedimentation tanks. Next sewage moves into tanks where lighter substances such as faeces settle to the bottom. This **sludge** is used to make fertilizer and methane gas. The liquid at the top, called **liquor** moves on to the next stage of treatment.

Rotating sprinkler

Clinker covered with bacteria and protozoa, which remove organic matter from liquor

Effluent

5 Biological filter

4 Aeration. Air is bubbled through the liquor to encourage growth of microbes such as bacteria. These digest wastes and change them into carbon dioxide and other harmless substances.

5 Biological filter. Then the liquor is sprinkled onto tanks filled with stones and clinker (the remains of burnt coal). These are covered with microbes which digest more wastes. This leaves a clean liquid called **effluent** which is pumped into rivers or the sea.

Questions

1 **a)** Name the three sources of water for drinking.
b) Which of these do you think has the cleanest and the dirtiest water. Give reasons.

2 Some cities pump untreated sewage into rivers and the sea. Think of ways this could harm people, and other living things.

We share the earth with millions of different living things. But we are destroying wildlife so fast that only the toughest species such as rats, mice, and sparrows may survive.

How wildlife is destroyed

1 Wildlife is destroyed when land is cleared for crops, farm animals, housing estates, roads, factories, mines, and quarries.
2 It is destroyed by pollution and waste tipping.
3 It is destroyed by people who hunt for fun, and to obtain things like ivory and furs which we can do without.

Some wildlife habitats

A **habitat** is a place where plants and animals live. Each habitat has its own collection of plants and animals.

Grassland can have twenty or more different grasses, and scores of different flowers. Hundreds of different insects may live there. Most wild grassland has been ploughed for crops, or seeded with fast-growing grasses for cattle.

Heathland is covered with heather, gorse, broom, billberry, lichens, mosses, and ferns. Snakes, lizards, and many birds live there. It is cleared mainly for commercial forestry, and sand and gravel quarries.

Wild woods contain oak, ash, beech, birch, shrubs, ferns, and many flowers. Most wild woods have been cleared to make way for crops or neat rows of spruce, pine, and other conifers.

Ponds and **marshes** are being drained and filled in so fast for crops and cattle that many of their plants, amphibia, birds and butterflies have become rare, and may soon disappear altogether.

How wildlife can be conserved

Over a hundred special wildlife habitats are destroyed in Britain every year. We need land to grow food, and for houses, factories, and roads. But we must not destroy all our wildlife to get it. Some places must be left untouched, for ever.

Farmers can help save wildlife by using pesticides only when it is really necessary. They can leave wild habitats untouched, and plant wild species of trees and shrubs in places where farming is difficult.

You too can help save wildlife, by following these rules:
1   Never uproot wild plants, or take birds' eggs.
2   Never leave fish hooks or lead weights where they can be swallowed by animals. The fish hooks will injure them and lead will poison them.
3   Never start fires or leave litter in the countryside.

Warning – toads crossing! Signs like these help preserve our wildlife.

To make up for the habitats we destroy, we must find ways to create new ones. An abandoned quarry makes an ideal wildlife habitat. This one has been turned into a nature park.

A wildlife garden. It contains only wild plants.

Ecology

Ecology is the study of habitats and the wildlife that lives in them. Ecologists find out which plants and animals live in each type of habitat. They study how each is adapted to live where it does. They are concerned about the environment. They advise farmers, industries and governments to consider the environment before making their development plans.

Questions
1   Describe some of the ways that habitats are being destroyed.

2   How can farmers conserve wildlife?
3   What can you do to protect wildlife?

Living things depend on other living things for food. They also depend on non-living things like sunlight, soil, water and air. They need these for energy, support, shelter and the raw materials of life.

Ecologists study the ways living things depend on each other and on the non-living world. They find the links in food chains and food webs. They look at how organisms are adapted to their way of life and how they are affected by climate, soil, landscape and pollution.

Communities

A **community** is a group of living things which share a habitat such as a rock pool, a pond, a meadow or a forest. Communities are made up of many kinds of animals and plants. A rock pool is the habitat of sea weeds, anemones, winkles, crabs, fish and so on.

Populations

A **population** is a number of creatures of the same kind. A forest may have populations of squirrels, owls, spiders, oak trees and bluebells.

Adaptations

Every living thing is adapted to live in a certain way. Lions have teeth for tearing flesh and crushing bones. Butterflies have long tubular mouths for sucking nectar from flowers. Most flowers have colour and scent to attract insects for pollination. An eagle's beak is adapted for tearing flesh.

A coral reef community is one of the richest on earth.

A population of penguins

Sundew leaves are adapted for catching insects.

Each type of tree has a different community of animals which feed off it or shelter in it. Nearly a hundred different creatures live on oak trees.

A population of periwinkles

An eagle's beak is adapted for tearing flesh.

The environment and living things

An organism's **environment** is all those things around it which affect its way of life, such as climate, landscape, soil, and other living things.

Climate. The number and kinds of creatures which live in a region depend on the amount of rain and sunshine there, and the average temperature. The animals and plants in hot dry regions are completely different from those in cool wet ones, or icy cold ones.

Landscape. The shape of the land affects living things because it causes local differences in climate. A river valley has a different climate from the top of a nearby mountain. The coast has a different climate than inland areas a few kilometres away.

Soil. Many plants are very choosy about the type of soil they will grow in. Sandy and clay soils, for instance, have very different plant populations, because sandy soils have large air spaces and dry out quickly, and clay soils have tiny air spaces and hold the water when it rains.

Other living things

Everywhere you look organisms affect the way other organisms live. Plants compete with each other for light and water. Animals feed on plants and on each other. Insects pollinate flowers, and animals disperse seeds. Humans clear land for farming, and pollute the environment.

Only tough plants like rock samphire and lichens can live on this exposed sea cliff.

The fence keeps out grazing animals. Note how this affects plant life.

Bluebells and wild garlic are plants which can live in the shade of woodland trees.

Questions

1 What are the differences between a community and a population? Give an example of each.

2 Explain how a sparrow is adapted for flying, perching, and eating seeds. How is it different from an eagle?

9·A Food chains, webs and pyramids

Trophic levels of food chains

The position of an organism on a food chain is called its **trophic level**. This position depends on whether it is a plant or an animal.

Green plants always occupy the **first trophic level** of a food chain because they are the producers which make the food which feeds the whole chain. The **second trophic level** is occupied by plant eaters (herbivores) and the **third and fourth trophic levels** are occupied by flesh eaters (carnivores). Study the diagram and text below.

Energy flows from one trophic level to the next as animals eat plants and each other.
1   What happens to energy at each trophic level (is it all passed to the next level)?
2   How does this explain why there are fewer consumers at each trophic level?
3   How does this explain why food chains rarely have more than four trophic levels?

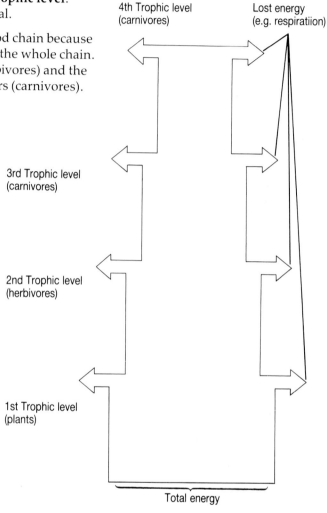

Flow of energy along food chains

There is a constant flow of energy along food chains but each consumer uses or wastes nearly all the energy it takes in. When a herbivore eats a plant it takes in only a small fraction of the energy the plant soaked up from the sun. Some was lost as heat as the plant respired, and some is lost as indigestible material which passes through the herbivore's gut. The same losses occur when carnivores eat herbivores, and to the end of the chain.

Energy loss at each trophic level limits the length of food chains because, by the fourth or fifth level there is no energy left to support another link, and it also gives rise to **biological pyramids**.

Food pyramids

The pyramid of numbers on page 164 is an example. Because of energy loss many oak leaves feed fewer caterpillars, which feed fewer robins and so on. But this pyramid is misleading because the leaves come from only *one plant*, the oak tree, so the pyramid should look like the diagram on the right. How would giving the *mass*, instead of the *number* of organisms at each level solve this problem?

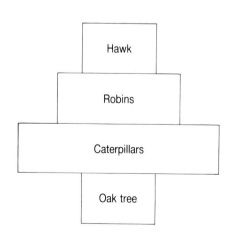

Pyramids of biomass

Food pyramids are more accurate if they show the total mass, or **biomass** of living things at each trophic level. Although there is only one oak tree it is large enough (has sufficient biomass) to support many herbivores and carnivores.

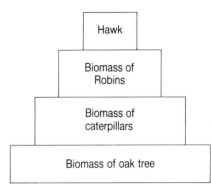

Polluted food chains

Pesticides like lindane, dieldrin and DDT endanger wildlife because they do not break down into harmless substances after use. They stay unchanged in the environment passing from one trophic level to the next along food chains and webs, weakening or killing animals all the way to the end.

DDT was developed to kill mosquitoes and was sprayed in such amounts that it is found everywhere in the world, even in the tissues of Antarctic penguins. DDT is banned in many areas but its replacement is expensive so it is still used in poor countries.

1 Pesticide sprayed onto a crop was washed by rain into a nearby pond, where its concentration in parts per million (ppm) was measured.

2 What happened to the pesticide as it passed along the food chain?

3 It takes about 10 g of biomass to support 1 kg of biomass in the next tropic level of food chain. Use this fact to explain the change in concentration of pesticide as it moved along the chain.

4 Why are consumers at the end of a chain more in danger than those at the beginning?

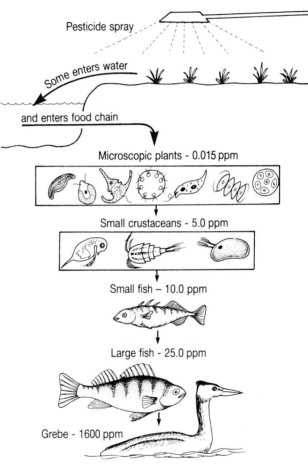

Food webs

Food webs are made up of many inter-connected food chains.

1 How many food chains can you find in this food web?

2 The farmer planted cereal seeds treated with fungicide. A year later hawk eggs had very thin shells. Formulate a hypothesis to explain this.

3 Children took away the frogs. How did it affect plants, insects, spiders, snakes and hawks?

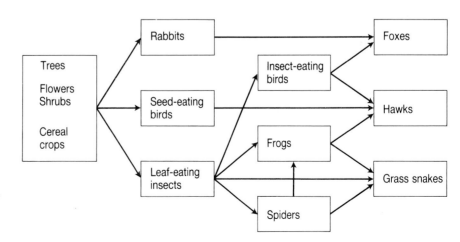

9·B The greenhouse effect

The world is warming up

There is mounting evidence that the world is getting warmer, and that this is caused by what scientists call **the greenhouse effect**. Study the text and diagram below to see what this means, then try to work out why the world is getting warmer.

1 Sunlight can pass through the glass of a greenhouse and is absorbed by the floor, earth and other contents. These warm up and radiate heat energy, in the form of infra-red radiation, which cannot escape through the glass, so it is trapped inside the greenhouse and warms it up.

2 Carbon dioxide in the earth's atmosphere acts like greenhouse glass: it lets sunlight through but stops infra-red radiation from the earth's surface escaping back into space. Atmospheric carbon dioxide is increasing because of air pollution.

3 How is the world similar to a greenhouse? From these facts try to form a hypothesis to explain why the world is warming up.

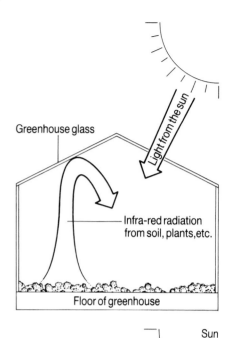

Since 1850 world temperatures have risen by about 0.5°C and could rise several degrees more by the year 2000. The reasons why this apparently small rise is causing alarm are discussed later. First you should understand why it is happening.

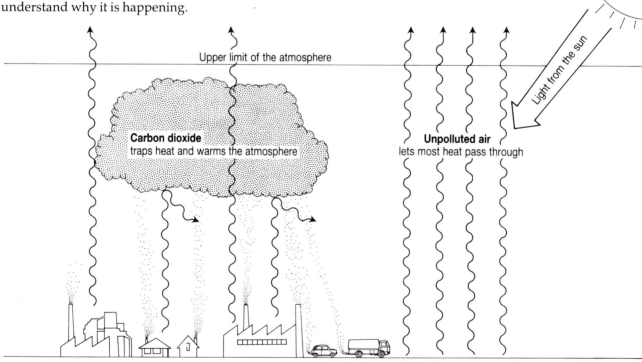

Sunlight warms up the earth's surface which emits infra-red radiation

Air behaves like the glass of a greenhouse: sunlight energy passes through and is absorbed by the earth's surface. This warms up and emits heat, in the form of infra-red radiation. In clean air some heat is absorbed by carbon dioxide and water vapour, but most escapes back into space.

Polluted air contains much more carbon dioxide than normal, together with pollutants such as methane, nitrous oxide and chlorofluorocarbons (CFC's). These 'greenhouse gases' absorb infra-red heat and radiate it back to the earth. So heat is trapped and warms the atmosphere.

The amount of carbon dioxide in the air should remain constant at about 0.003 per cent, but it is rising all the time. This is happening because our modern industrial society is producing it much faster than it can be absorbed by plants (see graph on the right).

It is estimated that at present rates of increase carbon dioxide pollution alone could raise world temperatures by 4.5°C by the year 2020. This does not allow for heat absorption by other 'greenhouse gas' pollutants, and an increased amount of water vapour due to faster evaporation from the sea.

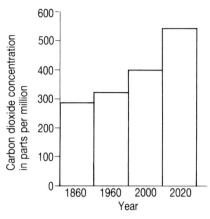

The effects of global warming

Study the text opposite before reading further.

Melting ice caps.   Temperature rises could be epecially high around the poles causing extensive melting of the ice caps and a rise in sea level. This is already happening. Glaciers are in retreat, and sea level has been rising since 1900. A rise of more than 1.5 metres is predicted by the year 2050, which would cause disastrous flooding of cities and farmland in low-lying areas such as East Anglia, Holland, Florida and the Ganges delta.

Make a few predictions about the effects of global warming:

1   What could happen to the ice caps, and how would this affect the continents?

2   What could happen to the weather?

3   How would plants be affected by extra warmth and carbon dioxide?

Climatic change.   Uneven heating of the world could cause already arid regions to become even drier. Central parts of North America, a vast food-producing area, could also become much drier.

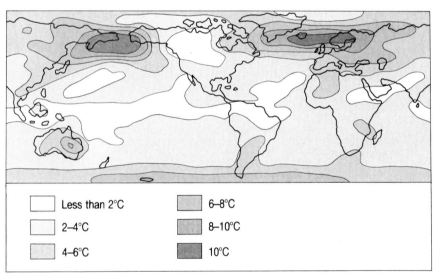

Effects on wildlife.   Creatures adapted to cool climates will have to spread northwards. Animals can do this quickly, but many plants could be killed by warming.

One computer model of the coming greenhouse warming. The effects will not be uniform

Effects on crop plants.   Weeds thrive on the extra carbon dioxide but some crop plants do not, so these will be more difficult to cultivate. Leaf tissue becomes less nutritious with increased carbon dioxide, so crop pests will eat far more.

Two ways of stopping the greenhouse effect

1   Improved pollution technology could remove most of the carbon dioxide from power station smoke. But the cost in equipment and lost power output would make electricity 50–70 per cent more expensive to produce.

2   Better insulation and more efficient use of power in homes and factories, together with development of renewable energy sources such as hydro-electric, geothermal, wind and wave power (page 175) would reduce coal demand by 58 per cent in the year 2050. Which of these alternatives is the best?

Air pollution and acid rain

The earth's atmosphere is about 900 km thick but living things are confined to a thin layer extending to only 3.2 km above the surface. It is in this layer that most pollutants gather.

Where air pollutants come from

The main source of air pollution is the burning of coal and oil in houses, factories, power stations and vehicle engines. When burned they produce soot and smoke, and a mixture of gases including sulphur dioxide, oxides of nitrogen, carbon monoxide, carbon dioxide and various hydrocarbons. Study the diagram and text opposite.

These pollutants rise on warm air currents. Some remain airborne for a long time and are carried hundreds of kilometres, some enter clouds and fall back to earth as rain (known as **wet deposition** or **acid rain**), and some fall back to earth as **dry depositions**.

This diagram shows the main sources of sulphur dioxide in Britain. Study page 173 then suggest how power station emission could be reduced. How could domestic emissions be reduced?

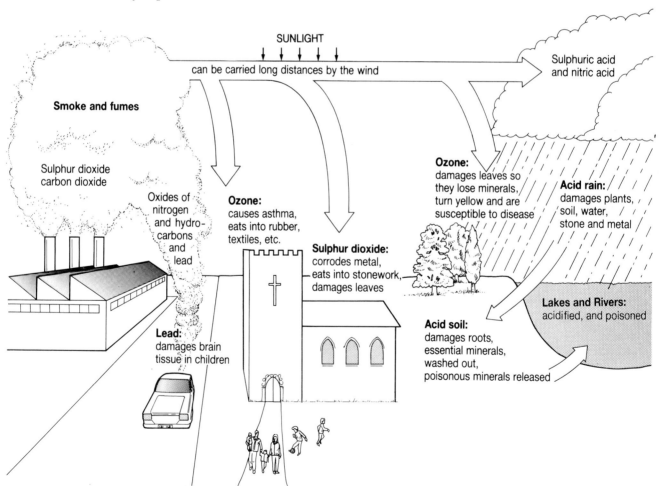

1   *How do power stations damage churches?*

2   *Which gases make acid rain?*

3   *How can car exhaust damage a child's brain?*

Dry deposition

Sulphur dioxide. This gas damages the waxy coating which protects leaves and prevents chlorophyll formation. It forms an acid vapour in the lungs, which aggravates diseases such as bronchitis. It corrodes exposed stonework causing a skin to form which flakes off, and changes the stone chemically so it crumbles away.

Oxides of nitrogen. These come mainly from vehicle exhaust fumes. They corrode metal and stone, and can have harmful effects on people with lung disease.

Hydrocarbons. These come from vehicle exhaust fumes and coal burning. Some, like benzophrene (also present in cigarette smoke), can cause cancer.

Ozone. This is formed by the action of sunlight on oxides of nitrogen and hydrocarbons. Ozone in the upper atmosphere shields the earth from harmful ultra violet rays, but near the ground it is a pollutant. It attacks plant leaves, weakening cell walls and allowing rain to wash away minerals, and stunts plant growth. It can also cause asthma attacks, and eats into materials such as rubber and textiles.

Wet deposition, or acid rain

When fumes enter a cloud they dissolve in water vapour and form sulphuric and nitric acid. Eventually these fall back to earth as acid rain.

Damage to plants. Acid rain and dry depositions are blamed for the death of trees and crop damage in Europe, Scandinavia and Britain. Leaves turn yellow and fall off, and roots are damaged so they cannot absorb minerals. This weakens plants so they are more likely to be killed by drought, severe winters and attacks from insects and fungi. These have a smaller effect on healthy plants.

Damage to soils. Acids cause essential minerals in soil to be washed away by rain, and release poisonous chemicals like aluminium and mercury, which are normally insoluble and harmless.

Damage to water life. At around pH6 shrimps and minnows disappear (these are food for larger fish). At pH5.6 the external skeletons of crayfish and their eggs soften so they are killed by fungi. Acids also wash aluminium and mercury from soils into the water where they poison fish and other water life.

Preventing acid rain

1   Coal and oil can be treated to remove some of their sulphur.
2   Chimneys can be fitted with smoke-cleaning equipment.
3   Furnaces can be designed to produce less pollution and become more efficient.
4   Car exhausts can be fitted with devices to remove pollutants.

Changes in the acidity of a Scottish loch since the year 1300. Scotland has mainly acid soils so at first it was claimed that rain water running out of these was the cause of acidified lakes. Does the graph above disprove this hypothesis? What other hypothesis does it suggest?

Air pollutants can spread from their source at 500 km a day. Norway and Sweden have accused Britain of 'exporting' acid rain to them. Find out the direction of prevailing winds in the area above and decide if this map supports their hypothesis.

187

Questions

1 *Recall knowledge*
Put each food chain in the correct order:
   a) water snail → humans → water weed → fish
   b) greenfly → rose leaf → ladybird
   c) worms → dead leaves → hawk → thrush
   d) slug → grass snake → frog → lettuce leaf

2 *Recall knowledge*
Below is a diagram showing part of the carbon cycle. What do the labels A, B, and C stand for?

3 *Recall knowledge*
Below is a diagram of the nitrogen cycle.
   a) How does clover help to convert nitrogen gas into soil nitrates (label A)?
   b) Name the soil bacteria which convert nitrogen gas into nitrates (label B).
   c) Describe one other way in which nitrogen gas is converted into nitrates (label C).
   d) How are animal proteins converted into nitrates (label D)?
   e) How are some soil nitrates converted back into nitrogen gas (label E)?

4 *Understanding*
Below is a map of a river.
   a) Why do fishermen catch more fish at point A than at point C?
   b) Many trees in the conifer plantation are dying. Why do you think this is?
   c) One day the sewage treatment works broke down, and untreated sewage entered the river. What happened to the amount of oxygen in the water at point B? Explain your answer. What effect would this have on water animals?
   d) When the farmer puts fertilizer on his crops, the water weeds at point C grow bigger. Explain why.
   e) Local fish-eating birds get sick when the farmer sprays his crops with pesticide. Explain why.

5 *Understanding*
In the autumn, the leaves fall off trees. But chemicals from the leaves may be taken back into a tree through its roots, and used for new leaves. Explain how this happens.

6 *Understanding/interpret data*

Radioactive materials were illegally dumped on a waste tip. Two types of organism began to decompose this material and gave off a radioactive gas. Some time later radioactivity was detected in plants growing nearby, and later still it spread to animals. The amount of radioactivity in two animals is shown in the graph opposite.

a) Name two decomposers.

b) What radioactive gas do you think the decomposers gave off?

c) What process in plants took in this radioactive gas, so that the plants became radioactive?

d) How could grasshoppers and spiders have become radioactive?

e) Why does the curve for spiders lag behind the curve for grasshoppers?

f) Why does the curve for spiders have a higher curve than the curve for grasshoppers?

g) What living processes may have led to the decrease in radioactivity?

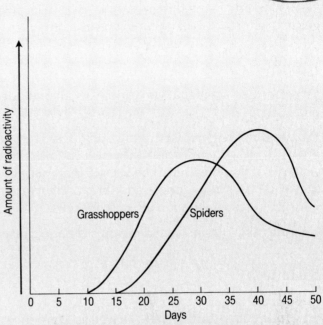

0 = The day radioactive material was dumped

7 *Understanding*

The diagram opposite shows the amount of energy which flows through living things in a grassland habitat each year.

a) What process in grass absorbs energy from the sun?

b) Calculate the difference between energy absorbed by the grass and the energy passed from grass to other living things. Give reasons for this difference.

c) What would happen to the habitat if decomposers could be removed?

8 *Understanding*

a) Which of the following food chains fits the pyramid of numbers opposite:

    a) grass → rabbits → fox

    b) tree → insects → birds

    c) phytoplankton → zooplankton → fish

    d) tree → monkeys → fleas

    e) grass → insects → birds

b) What is a pyramid of biomass?

c) Draw the pyramid opposite again so that it is a pyramid of biomass.

189

10·1 Germs, disease and infection

Germs are tiny living things that cause disease. All viruses are germs. Some bacteria and fungi are also germs.

Viruses

Viruses are so small that you cannot see them under an ordinary microscope.

Viruses don't respire, feed, grow, or move. They just reproduce. They can only do this inside the cells of another organism. For example, if you breathe in the viruses that cause the common cold they enter cells in your nose and throat. They turn these cells into virus factories which soon infect other cells.

Chicken pox, influenza, and measles are also caused by viruses.

Bacteria

Bacteria are larger than viruses, but still very small. Unlike viruses they feed, move, and respire, as well as reproduce. Bacteria which live as germs harm living things in two main ways.

1 They destroy living tissue. Tuberculosis is a disease caused by bacteria which destroy lung tissue.

2 They produce poisons, called **toxins**. Food poisoning is caused by bacteria which release toxins into the digestive system. Boils, whooping cough, and venereal disease are caused by bacteria.

Fungi

Some fungi cause diseases in humans. For example, **ringworm fungi** cause a disease called **ringworm**. This shows up as red rings on the scalp and on the groin. A similar fungus attacks the soft skin between the toes, causing **athlete's foot**.

The spread of infection

These are some of the ways you can be infected with germs:
1 By touching infected people, or things they have used such as towels, combs, and cups. Athlete's foot can be caught by walking on wet floors or mats used by infected people. Chicken pox and measles are spread by touching infected people.

2 By breathing in germs from infected people, especially when they cough or sneeze near you. So you should always cough and sneeze into a handkerchief. Colds, influenza, pneumonia, and whooping cough are spread by coughs and sneezes.

A photo of AIDS viruses, taken with false colour to show them up. The green and red blobs are the viruses. One is popping out of a white blood cell which it has just destroyed.

A special camera was used for this photo of a man sneezing. Note the air and droplets of mucus exploding from his nose and mouth. Can you see how coughs and sneezes spread germs?

3 From infected food and drink. Food and drink can be infected with germs by coughs and sneezes, dirty hands, flies, mice, and pet animals. Infected food and drink cause food poisoning and dysentery.

Preventing infection

These are some ways you can avoid being infected with germs.

1 Keep yourself clean.

 a) Wash your hair regularly. If you have dandruff or lice, use a special shampoo until it clears up.

 b) Wash your face regularly.

 c) Bathe or shower regularly, especially in hot weather.

 d) Clean your teeth at least once a day.

2 Change underwear and socks daily.

3 Boil water you think may be infected with germs.

4 Cook food thoroughly and eat it straight away. If you want to store it, keep it in the fridge.

Sexually Transmitted Diseases (STD)

Gonorrhoea, syphilis and herpes are all infections that are spread by sexual intercourse. The AIDS virus can also be spread by sexual intercourse, or by an infected person's blood getting into someone else's blood.

The risk of catching sexually transmitted diseases is greater the more sexual partners you have. Using a condom during intercourse can give some protection against most of them. The best protection is not to have intercourse with an infected person.

A victim of AIDS. The disease cannot be cured and so must be prevented from spreading. Wearing condoms during sex stops infection. People who use hypodermic needles should use sterilized ones.

Questions

1 List all the ways germs are being spread in the drawing above.

2 Why should you never use a stranger's towel?

3 Why should you sneeze into a handkerchief?

4 Why should you regularly wash between your toes?

5 Why must you cook food thoroughly?

191

10·2 Defences against disease

Your body has many ways of defending itself against viruses, bacteria and other germs. Together these defences give your body **natural immunity** against infection.

Your **nose and air passages** are lined with cells which make a sticky fluid called **mucus**. This traps germs and dirt from the air you breathe. Tiny hairs called **cilia** move the mucus, germs and dirt to your throat where they are swallowed and passed harmlessly out of your body.

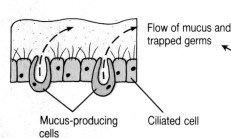

Flow of mucus and trapped germs

Mucus-producing cells

Ciliated cell

Your **skin** has an outer layer of dead cells which form a barrier against germs. **Sebaceous glands** under the skin make **sebum**, an oily antiseptic liquid which keeps skin supple, waterproof and protected from most germs.

Germs which get into wounds or your **blood stream** are eaten by white blood cells called **phagocytes**.

The lining of your **stomach** produces acid needed for digestion. This acid also kills germs which enter your body in food and drink.

Your **eyes** are protected against germs by an antiseptic liquid from your **tear glands**. Your eyes are washed with this liquid every time you blink.

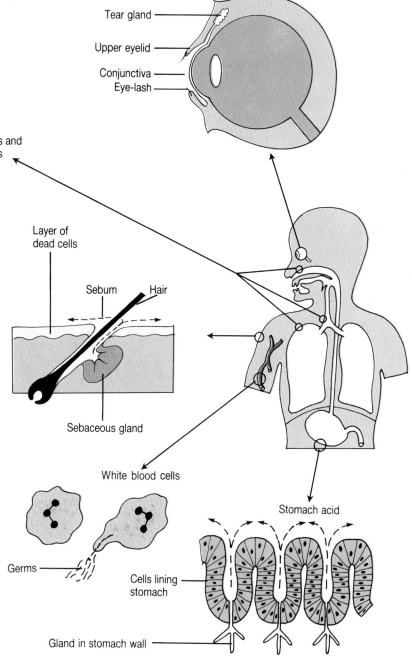

Tear gland
Upper eyelid
Conjunctiva
Eye-lash

Layer of dead cells
Sebum
Hair
Sebaceous gland

White blood cells
Germs

Stomach acid
Cells lining stomach
Gland in stomach wall

Antibodies – your body's chemical weapons

Bacteria, viruses and other germs have substances called **antigens** on their surface.

When your body detects antigens white blood cells called lymphocytes send out chemicals called **antibodies**.

Antibodies combine with the antigens. This kills the germs by making them burst or stick together, or by making it easier for phagocytes to eat them.

Each type of germ needs a different antibody to kill it. Some antibodies called **antitoxins** can destroy the poisons (toxins) which germs produce. Once an antibody is made it can stay in your body for several years making you immune to further attacks from the germs it destroys.

Artificial immunity

You don't have to catch a disease to make antibodies against it. You can be given a **vaccine** which makes your body produce antibodies so you are ready to fight off an infection before the germs arrive.

A vaccine contains either dead germs, harmless germs or a harmless germ toxin. When you are vaccinated your lymphocytes make antibodies just as if real germs had got into your body.

One of the first people to use a vaccine was Edward Jenner. In the early nineteenth century he proved that people who caught a mild disease called cowpox were then immune to a killer disease called smallpox.

He scratched the skin of a healthy boy and rubbed pus from a girl with cowpox into the wound. The boy caught cowpox. When he recovered Jenner inoculated him with pus from a smallpox victim, but the boy did not catch this disease. We now know that cowpox and smallpox germs have the same antigens, so the boy's body already contained the right antibodies to fight off the smallpox infection.

Questions

1 Explain how your eye, skin, air passages and gut fight off germs.

2 Describe two ways your blood fights germs.

3 John caught measles in 1986. His sister caught measles in 1987 but John didn't catch it again. Explain why, using technical words from this unit.

10·3 Smoking and ill-health

Smoking kills. In Britain nearly 100 000 people die each year from diseases caused by smoking. This is twelve times the number killed in road accidents.

Tobacco smoke is poison

Tobacco smoke contains about 1000 chemicals. Many of them are harmful. Here are some of the poisonous ones.

Nicotine is a poisonous drug. It damages the heart, blood vessels, and nerves. Smokers get addicted to it, which is why they find it hard to give up smoking.

Tar forms in the lungs when tobacco smoke cools. The tar contains 17 chemicals that are known to cause cancer in animals.

Carbon monoxide is a poisonous gas which stops blood carrying oxygen round the body.

Other poisonous gases in tobacco smoke are **hydrogen cyanide**, **ammonia**, and **butane**. These irritate the lungs and air passages, making smokers cough.

A section through a healthy human lung.

A section through the lung of a smoker. The spots are deposits of tar. They prevent the lungs from doing their job properly.

Diseases caused by smoking

Heart disease is three times more common among smokers than among non-smokers.

Emphysema is a disease in which lung tissue is destroyed by the chemicals in tobacco smoke. The lungs develop large holes which blow up like balloons. Breathing becomes very difficult.

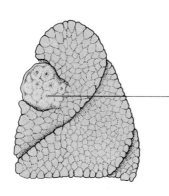

The swelling on this lung is due to emphysema, caused by heavy smoking.

Cancers of the lungs, mouth, gullet, and bladder are caused by chemicals called **carcinogens** in tobacco smoke.

Nine out of ten people who die of lung cancer are smokers.

Bronchitis is mostly a smoker's disease. Smoke irritates the air passages to the lungs, making them swollen and sore. Tiny hairs called cilia usually keep these passages clear. But the cilia stop working, so the lungs fill with mucus.

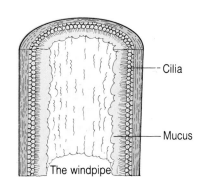

Cilia

Mucus

The windpipe

The cilia which keep your lungs and air passages clean stop working when you smoke.

Smokers get up other people's noses

Many non-smokers find tobacco smoke very unpleasant. It makes eyes sting, and can cause sore throats and headaches. It can irritate babies and people with hayfever and asthma.

Non-smokers who work or live with smokers can suffer lung damage and other smokers' diseases.

Pregnant mothers who smoke have smaller babies than non-smoking mothers. They also run the risk of a more difficult birth.

Smokers smell. Their breath, hair, clothes, and homes have a horrible smell caused by the ammonia, tar, and other chemicals in smoke.

Questions

1 Work out how much it costs to buy 20 cigarettes a day for a year. List the things you could buy if you saved this amount by giving up smoking.

2 Which chemical in smoke is addictive?

3 What harm does carbon monoxide do?

4 What is emphysema?

5 List three other diseases linked with smoking.

6 Why is it bad for pregnant mothers to smoke?

10·4 Health warning

Most people don't drink too much, or sniff glue, or take drugs like heroin and cocaine. But everyone should know the harm these things do.

Drugs and their effects

Heroin is made from opium poppies. It gives a feeling of power and contentment. But when this wears off, users become anxious and depressed. So they take more heroin to feel better. Soon they feel they cannot live without it. They are now heroin addicts.

Cocaine is made from the leaves of the coca bush. At first it gives a feeling of energy and strength. But after about 20 minutes users feel confused and anxious. They are unable to sleep for some time.

LSD is made from a fungus. Users may see things around them changing in colour, shape, and size. Or they may see things which are not there (hallucinations). Sometimes the hallucinations are very unpleasant, and are called **bad trips**. They can cause fear, depression, and mental illness.

Cannabis is made from the leaves and resin of the Indian hemp plant. Users seem to see, hear, feel and think more clearly. But they can become confused and do reckless and dangerous things.

Solvent and glue sniffers breathe in fumes from things like glue, paint, and cleaning fluid. They get a floating feeling and hallucinations. But the fumes get into the blood and damage the heart. They also cause sickness, depression, and bad facial acne.

Infections. Some drugs are taken by injection. Dirty needles can cause sores, abscesses, blood poisoning, and jaundice. AIDS can be passed from one person to another if needles are shared.

Addiction. Drugs can cause addiction. People feel they cannot live without the drug. They may turn to crime to get money for it. Once you are addicted to a drug, giving up becomes a difficult and painful experience. People begin taking drugs to feel good, they end up having to take drugs to stop feeling very bad. Drug addicts cause themselves and their families great unhappiness and stress.

Addicts can get help from Family Doctors who sometimes recommend hospital treatment. Support groups exist to help addicts and their families cope, and they may suggest ways of curing addiction.

196

The risks of taking drugs

Overdoses. A drug overdose can cause unconsciousness, damage to the heart and other organs, and even death. It is easy to take an overdose by accident, because it is hard to tell how strong a drug is, or how much to take. Drugs are far more dangerous when they are mixed. Their effects are multiplied, so a much lower dose can kill.

Mental harm. A drug user may suffer strong feelings of anger and fear, or terrifying hallucinations. This can cause mental damage.

Changes in behaviour. Drug users can become irritable, and lose interest in their friends, hobbies, and work. They may stop looking after themselves.

Accidents. People taking drugs run the risk of accidents, because they get confused. They can fall into water and drown, or walk in front of traffic, or fall out of windows. Glue sniffers can suffocate while their mouths are covered by plastic bags, or choke to death on their own vomit.

Alcohol

All alcoholic drinks contain a chemical called ethanol. This is what makes people drunk.

1 Ethanol is carried to the brain by the blood. From there it affects all the nervous system. A little ethanol makes people feel pleasant and relaxed. But if they keep drinking they feel dizzy and cannot walk straight. Speech becomes slurred and they begin to see double. They may become quarrelsome. Eventually they cannot stand up. If they drink more they become unconscious, and may even die.

2 Even a little alcohol causes people to make mistakes in things like typing and driving. It is very dangerous to drink and drive.

3 The effects of ethanol can last for hours. It takes about an hour for the body to get rid of the ethanol in just half a pint of beer.

4 Heavy drinking over a long period causes the brain to shrink. It can also cause stomach ulcers, cancers of the digestive system, and liver and heart disease.

5 Some people become addicted to alcohol. They turn into alcoholics.

6 If a woman is pregnant, ethanol in her blood is carried to the baby. It can damage the baby's brain and heart, and slow its growth.

Questions

1 Some drugs, and alcohol, are addictive. What does this mean?

2 Write down ten things you could say to convince a friend not to take drugs.

3 List the changes which take place in the body of a heavy drinker.

4 What changes in a person's behaviour can tell you that he or she may be taking drugs?

10·A Sexually transmitted diseases

Sexually transmitted, or **venereal diseases** (VD), are those which pass from person to person during sexual intercourse. Because of this, control of these diseases involves social as well as medical problems, so it is very important to discuss them openly. Before you can do this you must know how each disease is passed on, its symptoms and how to avoid risk of infection.

Syphilis and gonorrhoea are diseases caught only by sexual contact. Acquired Immunodeficiency Syndrome (AIDS) is passed on mainly by sexual contact but there are other ways of becoming infected.

Syphilis

This is a quite rare disease but is increasing, especially among young homosexual men. It affects more men than women. Early stages can be cured with antibiotics such as penicillin but are often difficult to detect. Symptoms usually appear 14 to 28 days after contact with an infected person, and the disease has three stages.

Stage one. Sores appear around the sex organs, anus or mouth. The sores look like craters which vary in size between a pinhead and a pea, and have a red centre. They are painless and soon disappear without treatment.

Stage two. This is a rash which can appear weeks or months after the first stage. It too is painless and soon disappears.

Stage three. This appears years later if the early stages go untreated and includes blindness, heart disease and insanity.

It is the fact that the early stages of syphilis are painless and often go unnoticed and untreated which makes this disease so dangerous. Remember, syphilis can only be treated in its early stages, and it is only during this time that the disease is infectious.

A pregnant woman with syphilis can pass the disease to her unborn baby. The baby often dies in the womb or soon after birth. If it does survive it can develop deafness and poor vision later in life.

Answer the questions opposite.

1 Think of two reasons why it is important that syphilis is detected and treated in its early stages.
2 Why should someone with several sexual partners never ignore skin sores?
3 Why is early detection of syphilis especially important among pregnant women?
4 What connection could there be between development of the contraceptive pill and an increase in the number of people with venereal disease.

Gonorrhoea

This is far more common than syphilis and the number of cases is increasing. It affects both males and females and all cases can be cured.

Symptoms appear about ten days after contact with an infected person. In men the symptoms include a burning sensation during urination (passing water) followed by a greenish-yellow discharge from the tip of the penis. The same symptoms can appear in women but, unfortunately, two out of three have no symptoms at all when infected and may only know of the disease when their partner develops symptoms.

1 Think of one difference between gonorrhoea and syphilis which makes the first more important (people should be more careful to avoid it)?
2 Why should women with several sexual partners have regular checks for gonorrhoea even if they have no symptoms?

Later stages of the disease include inflammation of the lining of the heart, inflammation of the joints (arthritis) and damage to the iris of the eye. A baby can pick up gonorrhoea from an infected mother as it passes through the vagina during birth.

Acquired immunodeficiency syndrome – AIDS

AIDS is caused by the **Human Immunodeficiency Virus** (HIV). HIV attacks the body's immune system destroying **T-cells**, a type of white blood cell which produces **antibodies**, the chemicals which destroy germs. This leaves AIDS patients open to normally harmless diseases which uninfected people fight off without difficulty.

AIDS patients are killed by chronic pneumonia and diarrhoea; fungus infections which block the throat, intestine and lungs; cancer of the skin and bone, and swelling of the brain. The AIDS virus itself can destroy brain tissue causing loss of memory, personality changes, and death. At present there is no cure for AIDS.

How you can get AIDS.   AIDS is passed on by sexual contact and by contact with body fluids.
1   During sexual intercourse the virus can pass from a man's semen to a woman (or to a man during homosexual contacts), or from a woman's vaginal fluid to a man.
2   HIV is found in the blood of AIDS patients, so you can be infected if their blood gets into your body.
a) This can happen when drug misusers share needles and syringes. The virus can also pass from person to person on unsterilized tattooing, ear-piercing and acupuncture equipment.
b) You may also be infected by sharing a razor or toothbrush with an infected person (gums can bleed when teeth are cleaned vigorously).
c) A pregnant woman can pass the virus to her developing baby through the placenta.

How you cannot get AIDS.   You cannot get AIDS by sharing a home, school or workplace with an infected person; by touching them or breathing the same air; or by using the same shower, cutlery, furniture, swimming pool or toilet as an infected person.

1   Why is the danger of VD and AIDS infection increased if you have many sexual partners?
2   How do you think condoms reduce the risk of infection?
3   Why is it dangerous for drug users to share hypodermic needles?
4   Why is it dangerous to share razors and toothbrushes with strangers?
5   Why should acupuncture and tattooing establishments thoroughly sterilize their equipment after each customer?
6   Why should first-aid workers wear rubber gloves when dealing with patients who are bleeding?
7   Why should spilt blood be washed away with water containing bleach?
8   Why is it a good idea to urinate (pass water) and wash the sex organs after sexual intercourse?
9   Why is it very important to see a doctor, or visit a VD clinic immediately signs of infection appear? Remember, VD clinic staff are trained to give sympathetic treatment, and not lectures on morals.
10   If a friend became an AIDS patient why would it be unnecessary and wrong to avoid all contact with him or her? Give reasons for your answer.

Cumulative totals up to end January 1987

The AIDS virus bursting out of a white blood cell

10·B Cancer

First answer the questions on the right, then read this unit to see how many you got right.

What is cancer?

Cancer is not one disease. There are over 200 different types each affecting different parts of the body, but they all begin in roughly the same way.

Every cell has genes which control cell division. These genes are 'switched on' when new cells are needed to replace cells that wear out or die. When the right number of cells have been produced the genes 'switch off' and cell division stops.

Sometimes these genes are damaged or altered. This can be caused by chemicals, radiation or viruses.

*1 Pick out **one** item from the list below which you think is the most important cause of cancer.*
alcohol
smoking
diet
food additives
sexual intercourse
pollution
industrial chemicals
germs

2 The number of people with cancer is increasing (true or false?)

3 Cancer can't be prevented (true or false?)

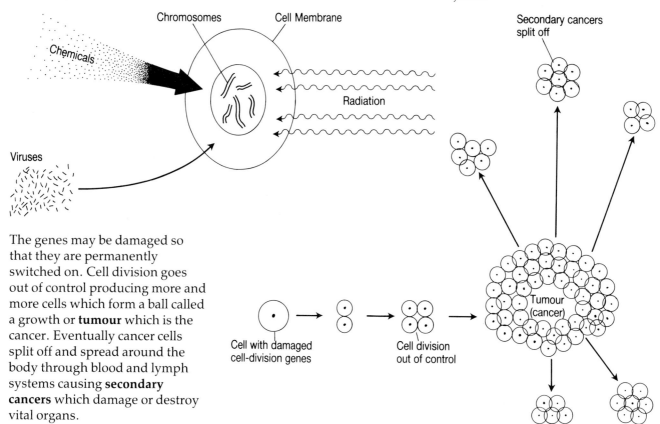

The genes may be damaged so that they are permanently switched on. Cell division goes out of control producing more and more cells which form a ball called a growth or **tumour** which is the cancer. Eventually cancer cells split off and spread around the body through blood and lymph systems causing **secondary cancers** which damage or destroy vital organs.

Is the number of people with cancer rising?

Answer this question from the figures opposite. What can you conclude about deaths from different types of cancer, and cancer deaths as a whole? Think of possible reasons for the changes since 1921 shown on this table.

	Lung cancer	Breast cancer	Other cancer	All cancers
1921–5	0.05	0.26	2.21	2.54
1941–5	0.32	0.26	1.80	2.38
1961–5	0.77	0.27	1.48	2.52
1981	0.68	0.32	1.38	2.38

Deaths per thousand middle-aged people (35–60 yrs) in England and Wales

What are the main causes of cancer?

Study the graph opposite to answer this question. Many people think that radiation, chemicals and pollution are the main causes of cancer. In fact eight out of ten cancers could be prevented if people did not smoke (Unit 10.3) and avoided certain foods. Here are some facts and a little advice.

Fat and salt. Fat may help the development of cancers in two ways. First, the more fat you eat the more bile acids your liver produces and these may irritate the lining of the bowel and stimulate cancer growth. Second, fat has an effect on the way breasts and other organs respond to hormones, which may set off cancer growth. Avoid, or cut down on fatty foods described in Unit 6.2. Excess salt has been linked with stomach cancer.

Alcohol. There is a clear link between excessive drinking of alcohol and cancer of the mouth, throat, larynx and gullet. If drinkers also smoke the risk of all these cancers is greatly increased.

Radiation. Some rocks are naturally radioactive, like the granites of Cornwall and Scotland. Radiation also comes from medical X-rays, nuclear reactors and waste dumps. All radiation, no matter how small, can set off cancer growth. The higher the level of radiation the greater the risk.

Sexual activity. Male semen can cause cancer by damaging cells in the cervix (see diagram on page 149). It is essential that all females with regular sexual partners attend a clinic for cervical examination (screening) about every three years.

Dietary fibre. There are fewer cancers of the bowel in areas such as Africa and Asia where fibre is an important part of the diet. A possible reason is that fibre absorbs poisonous wastes in food.

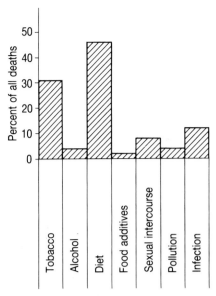

The main causes of cancer

Treatment of cancer

Each year 60 000 cancer sufferers receive treatment allowing them to return to a normal active life. If found early enough most cancers are easily treated.

Lasers. Skin and cervical cancer can be treated with laser beams. These are directed onto the cancer cells and shrivel them up. This is almost painless and requires no anaesthetic.

Surgery. Some cancers can be removed by cutting them out. The success of this method depends on how far the cancer has spread.

Chemotherapy. Cancer cell metabolism is much faster than ordinary cells. So, if carefully calculated doses of poison are injected into the blood they take up more poison than normal cells and die.

Radiotherapy. Radiation can start cancer but it can also be used to kill it. If beamed directly onto cancer cells they shrivel and die.

New treatments. New chemicals, antibodies and vaccines are being developed to fight cancer. You can help by supporting the Cancer Research Campaign.

Study these warning signs:

1 Bad, persistent cough or hoarseness.
2 Skin sores or ulcers which do not heal.
3 Unusual bleeding from the anus, or when passing water.
4 A lump especially in the breast, neck, armpit or testicles.
5 Any unexplained weight loss.
6 Change in a wart or mole.

Don't panic if you have one of these symptoms, it is most likely a simple infection.

'People die because of ignorance, fear and inaction.' Think of reasons why this statement is true.

1 *Understanding/interpret data*

This diagram shows how bacteria are affected by temperature.

a) Between which temperatures do bacteria multiply the fastest?

b) The temperature inside the main part of a refrigerator is about 4°C. Why is it unwise to keep foods, like meat, in this part of a refrigerator for more than three days?

c) The temperature in a domestic freezer is about −20°C. Why is it unwise to keep food in a freezer for more than three months?

d) Bacteria reproduce by dividing in two. If they have food and warmth they do this about every 30 minutes. If just one 'food-poison' bacterium landed on a piece of meat, and reproduced at this rate, how many would there be after 24 hours?

e) It is dangerous to cook a large piece of frozen meat before it has thawed out properly. Explain why.

- All bacteria killed — 100°C
- Many killed — 90°C
- 80°C
- 70°C
- 60°C
- 50°C
- Bacteria grow and multiply rapidly → 40°C
- 30°C
- 20°C
- 10°C
- Bacteria grow slowly with some multiplication → 0°C
- −10°C
- −20°C
- Bacteria live but do not multiply →

2 *Recall knowledge/understanding*

Why should you:

a) never use someone else's comb or towel?

b) always wash your hands after visiting the lavatory?

c) always wash your hands before handling food for other people?

d) never drink water from a pond or stream?

e) never bathe in the sea near a sewage pipe?

3 *Understanding*

Here is some advice for people who want to give up smoking.

a) Give up smoking at the same time as a friend does.

b) Every day, put the money you would have spent on cigarettes in a money box.

c) Eat fruit or raw carrots, or chew gum whenever you feel the urge for a cigarette.

d) Tell everyone you know that you are giving up smoking.

Take each piece of advice in turn, and explain why it is worth trying.

4 *Interpret data*

What do people know about alcohol? Try this 'true or false' test on as many people as possible, then give them the correct answers. Draw histograms to show the number of correct and incorrect answers.

a) Drinking beer is less harmful than drinking wine or spirits. (False – all alcoholic drinks can be as harmful as each other.)

b) If a man and a woman drink the same amount of alcohol, the woman will be more affected than the man. (True – on average it takes less alcochol to damage a woman's health than a man's.)

c) Alcohol is a stimulant. (False – alcohol dulls the brain.)

d) Alcohol warms you up. (False – alcohol enlarges blood vessels in your skin so you may feel warmer when in fact your body is losing heat more quickly.)

e) Three pints of beer can put someone over the legal blood alcohol limit for driving. (True – an average-sized adult reaches the legal blood alcohol limit for driving after drinking about two-and-a-half pints of beer.)

5 *Interpret data/recall knowledge*

The graph below shows the number of men aged 40–79 who die from lung cancer.

a) How many times is a cigarette smoker more likely to die of lung cancer than a non-smoker?

b) Suggest hypotheses to explain why cigarette smoking is more dangerous than cigar smoking.

c) Why do some non-smokers die of lung cancer?

d) Name other diseases caused by smoking.

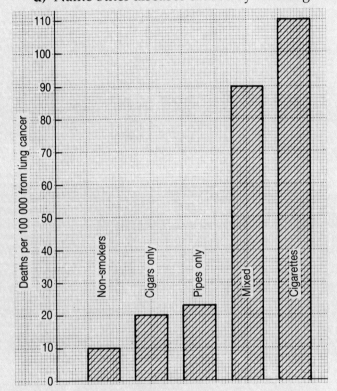

6 *Design/interpret data*

Write a report on drug abuse in your area, or in the UK as a whole. You could get information for your report in the following ways:

a) Newspaper and magazine cuttings. Over a period of several months cut out any articles about drug abuse.

b) Interview people. Ask if you can interview the local police, a doctor, hospital staff, and District Health Authority staff, to obtain information about local drug problems. Some of these people may agree to visit your school and talk to your class.

c) Visit a local hospital (arrange it in advance) to ask what percentage of casualty patients became injured under the influence of drink or drugs.

7 *Understanding*

Read the paragraph below, then answer the questions.

'AIDS is caused by a virus which can only live in blood, semen, and vaginal fluid. People can only catch the AIDS virus through sexual intercourse with an infected person, or by getting infected blood into their bloodstream.'

a) What is semen, and what is the vagina?

b) Why is it impossible to get AIDS by touching someone, or from cups, toilet seats, cutlery, clothes, door knobs or swimming pools?

c) Why does having many sexual partners increase the risk of catching the AIDS virus?

d) Why do drug addicts who inject themselves and share needles, increase their chances of catching the AIDS virus?

e) Why does the use of a condom reduce the risk of catching the AIDS virus?

8 *Design/interpret data*

Investigate the smoking habit in your school. Circulate a questionnaire and use students' answers to make graphs and charts to illustrate your results. Make it clear that nobody will see anyone else's answers. Here are a few of the things you could try to find out.

a) How many smokers, non-smokers, and ex-smokers are there in your school? Calculate the percentage of each type.

b) What is the age of each smoker? Draw a histogram to show 'numbers of smokers' against 'age'.

c) Why do smokers smoke? Design a questionnaire with four or five reasons on it and ask students to choose the one that's true for them. Write a report on your findings. Do your answers vary with age and sex?

d) How many smokers would like to give up the habit? What percentage is this of the total number of smokers?

e) How many smokers are *trying* to give up? What percentage is this of the total number of smokers?

Index

If more than one page number is given, you should look up the **bold** one first.

Acknowledgements

The publishers wish to thank the following for permission to reproduce transparencies:

Heather Angel: pp. 14 (centre), 172 (bottom centre), 179 (top); **Ardea**: pp. 171 (top), /**Ian Beames**: p. 60 (right), /**Liz & Tony Bomford**: p. 171 (bottom left), /**Ake Lindar**: p. 171 (centre), /**P. Morris**: p. 2 (centre), /**Wolfgang Wagner**: p. 21 (right); **Aspect Picture Library**: pp. 196 (top), 197 (top), /**Derek Bayes**: p. 172 (centre right); **Brian Beckett**: pp. 2 (top right), 3 (top right and bottom right), 10 (bottom left and bottom right), 11 (bottom left), 13 (bottom left, 14 (centre left), 15 (top right, centre left and bottom right), 18 (centre), 20 (all), 21 (top left, top centre and bottom left), 42 (centre left), 50 (both), 53 (left and centre), 55 (left and centre), 58, 59 (top left, top right and bottom right), 61 (both), 62 (top left, bottom left and bottom right), 63 (top centre, bottom left and bottom right), 64 (centre left, centre right, bottom left, bottom centre and bottom right), 65, 66 (all), 68 (all), 69 (left), 74 (bottom), 80 (bottom), 108 (centre left and bottom left), 112 (top right, centre and left), 113 (bottom), 129, 165, 167, 172 (top), 173 (centre), 179 (left); **Biphoto Associates**: pp. 43 (top left), 63 (bottom centre), 108 (top right); **Neil Bromhall**: p. 152 (bottom); **Bruce Coleman Ltd**: p. 18 (bottom); **Colorsport**: pp. 3 (top left), 78, 81; **Gene Cox**: p. 41; **Daily Telegraph Colour Library/P. Beney**: p. 166; **Fauna & Flora Preservation Society**: p. 179 (right); **Sally & Richard Greenhill**: pp. 34 (right), 108 (top left), 148 (both), 156, 171 (bottom right), 173 (centre right); **Holt Studios Ltd**: pp. 42 (bottom left & bottom right), 62 (top centre); **Chris Honeywell**: pp. 39 (left), 62 (top right), 69 (right), 80 (top), 82, 91 (top), 93, 94 (top), 96 (left), 98 (left), 100 (top), 109 (all), 112 (right), 118, 121 (centre), 132, 155 (all), 195; **Imperial Chemical Industries**: p. 120 (top left); **International Coffee Organization**: p. 157 (bottom); **John Radcliffe Hospital, Medical Illustration Dept.**: p. 121 (top); **Rob Judges**: pp. 37 (both), 64 (top right); **Andrew Lawson**: p. 137 (both); **Network**: /**Mike Abrahams** p. 197 (bottom), /**Mike Goldwater** 172 (bottom right); **Oxford Scientific Films Ltd**: /**Doug Allan** p. 18 (top right); /**Kathie Atkinson** p. 19 (bottom right), /**G.I. Bernard** pp. 2 (bottom right), 12 (top centre and bottom left), 13 (bottom centre and bottom left), 15 (top left and centre right), 16 (bottom right), 17 (top right, centre left and bottom left), 18 (left), 34 (left), 43 (bottom left and bottom right), 51, 55 (right), 62 (bottom centre), 63 (top left), 75 (right), 77 (both), 133 (left), 146 (bottom right); /**David & Sue Cayless** p. 178 (bottom right); **J.A.L. Cooke** pp. 3 (bottom left), 6 (both), 11 (top left and bottom centre), 13 (top centre and top right), 15 (bottom left), 75 (left), 178 (left); /**Rob Cousins** p. 157 (top); /**Stephen Dalton** pp. 2 (top left), 14 (top right), 16 (top right); /**Michael Fogden** p. 17 (bottom right); /**Phillip Goddard** p. 178 (top); /**Christian Hvidt/Foci** p. 52 /**Manfred Kage** p. 120 (top right); /**David Kerr** p. 53 (right); /**Caroline Kroeger/Animals Animals** p. 99; /**Z. Lesczyski/Animals Animals** p. 133 (right); /**G.A. Maclean** p. 178 (bottom centre); /**Mantis Wildlife Films** p. 153 (right); /**Sean Morris** p. 146 (bottom left); /**Peter O'Toole** p. 128; /**Richard Packwood** pp. 10 (bottom centre), 19 (bottom left), 63 (top right); /**Peter Parks** pp. 10 (top left and top right), 11 (inset), 12 (top right), 14 (centre right), 16 (bottom left), 45 (all), 74 (top), 91 (bottom), 146 (top left); /**Avril Ramage** p. 17 (top left); /**Michael Silver** p. 19 (top); /**David Thompson** pp. 3 (bottom centre), 13 (top left), 18 (centre right), 59 (bottom left), 147, 169; /**Gerald Thompson** pp. 11 (bottom), 16 (bottom centre), 21 (bottom centre); /**Maurice Tibbles** p. 19 (centre left); / **Barry Walker** p. 18 (centre left); /**Barrie Watts** p. 11 (top right); /**Nick Woods** p. 14 (bottom left); **Oxford University Press**: pp. 36, 38, 39 (right), 98 (bottom right), 114; **Picturepoint Ltd**: p. 173 (top); **Poly**: p. 42 (top and centre right); **Reflex Pictures/Philip Gordon**: p. 196 (bottom); **Science Photo Library**: pp. 89 (both), 113 (top); /**Michael Abbey** p. 10 (top centre), /**Dr Tony Brain** p. 28 (bottom left); /**Dr Arnold Brody** p. 95 (top); /**Dr Jeremy Burgess** pp. 29 (right), 60 (left); /**Dr Colin Chumbley** p. 138 (bottom); /**CNRI** p. 12 (bottom right), 28 (bottom centre), 34 (top), 94 (bottom); 95 (bottom); 98 (top); /**CNRI/Professor Montagnier, Institut Pasteur** p. 190 (top); /**Eric Grave** pp. 28 (top), 146 (top right); /**Richard Hutchings** p. 43 (top right); / **Manfred Kage** pp. 28 (bottom right), 138 (top); /**Hank Morgan** p. 100 (bottom); /**Larry Mulvehill** p. 92; /**Petit Format/Nestle** p. 153 (left and centre); /**David Scharf** p. 150; /**Dr Gary Settles** p. 190 (bottom); /**St. Stephens's Hospital, Department of Medical Photography** p. 191; /**James Stevenson** p. 96 (right), 194 (both); /**R.B. Taylor** p. 29 (left); **Supersport Photographs/Eillen Langley** p. 108 (top centre); **Patricia Taylor** p. 172 (bottom left).

Diagrams by: **Brian Beckett**

Additional Illustrations by: **David Holmes, Peter Joyce, Frank Kennard, Ed McLachlan, R.D.H. Artists.**

Oxford University Press, Walton Street, Oxford OX2 6DP
Oxford New York Toronto
Delhi Bombay Calcutta Madras Karachi
Petaling Jaya Singapore Hong Kong Tokyo
Nairobi Dar es Salaam Cape Town
Melbourne Auckland
and associated companies in
Berlin Ibadan

Oxford is a trade marks of Oxford University Press

© *B. S. Beckett and R. M. Gallagher 1989*
First published 1989
Reprinted 1990
ISBN 0 19 914317 X

Typeset by Tradespools Ltd., Frome, Somerset, UK
Printed in Hong Kong